GCSE Revision Notes

Revision Notes

GCSE Physics

Author
PAUL LEVY
Series editor **ALAN BREWERTON**

Contents

Electricity and magnetism

Forces and motion

Waves

The Earth and beyond

Energy resources and energy transfer

Radioactivity

Electricity and magnetism

Electrostatics

- **Static electricity** – electric charges stationary
- **Charges** – positive (+) or negative (–)
- **Insulators** – substances in which electricity cannot flow e.g. plastics
- **Conductors** – substances in which electricity can flow e.g. metals – some electrons can move freely
- **Electron transfer** – two insulators rubbed together
- **Insulator + electrons** → negative charge (–)
- **Insulator – electrons** → positive charge (+)

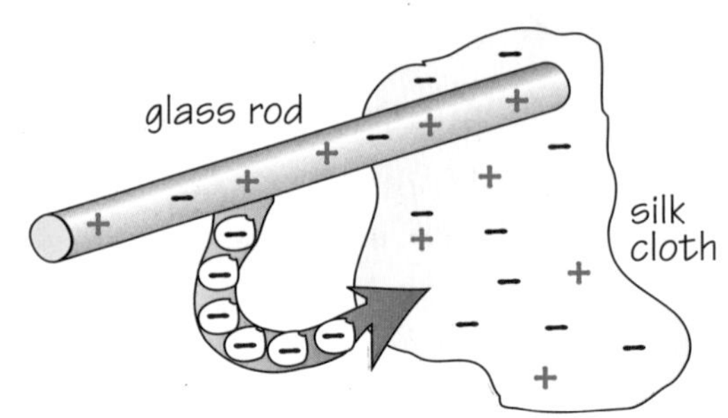

electrons move from the rod to the cloth

Charged objects

- **Like charges repel** + and + or – and –
- **Unlike charges attract** + and –
- **Charged objects attract uncharged** objects
- **Greater charge** – greater voltage between object and Earth
- **High voltage** – spark may jump gap

Unlike magnetic poles also attract

Applications

Electrostatic filters – used to clean smoky chimneys
Aircraft fuel lines – earthed to avoid sparks/fire

Examiner's tip
You need to be able to describe dangers and uses

Electrostatic painting

- Panel connected to Earth, gives it –ve charge
- +ve charge given to powder
- Powder attracted to panel

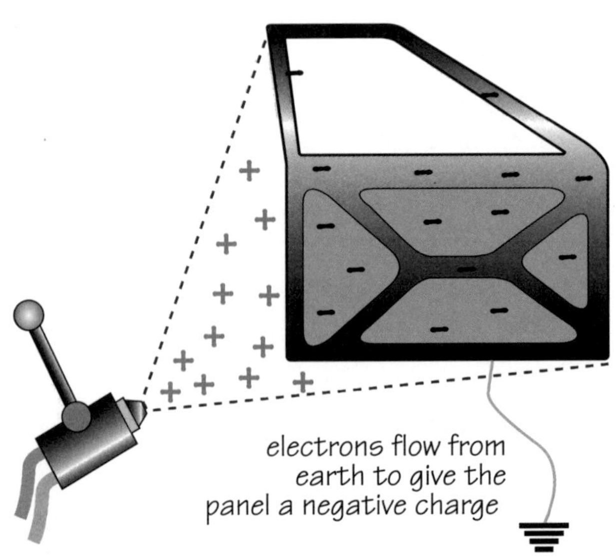

electrons flow from earth to give the panel a negative charge

Electrolysis

- **Ionic compounds** e.g. Sodium Chloride NaCl **conduct electricity** when molten or dissolved in water
- **Negative (–) ions flow to anode** (positive electrode)
- **Positive (+) ions flow to cathode** (negative electrode)
- **Substances deposited/released at electrodes**

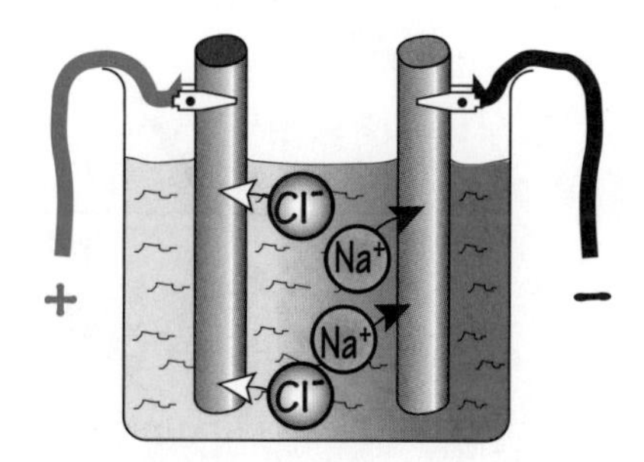

- **Amount of substance deposited/released greater when**
  - the size of the current greater
  - the time for which the current flows greater

Current electricity

Resistance

- **Current electricity** – (negative) electric charges move
- **Resistance** – anything that hinders movement
- **Resistance of conductor greater** – conductor longer or thinner
  – conductor hotter

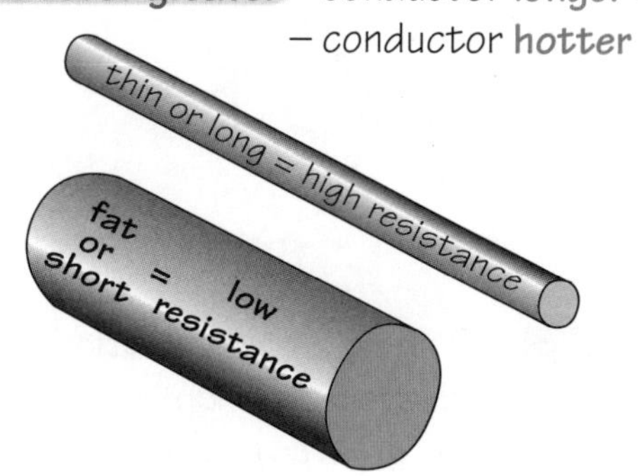

- **Resistance different** – different materials e.g. copper and lead

$$\text{resistance} = \frac{\text{voltage}}{\text{current}}$$

- **Units** – ohms (Ω)
- **Ohm's law** – resistance constant
- **Resistors heated** – charge flows through

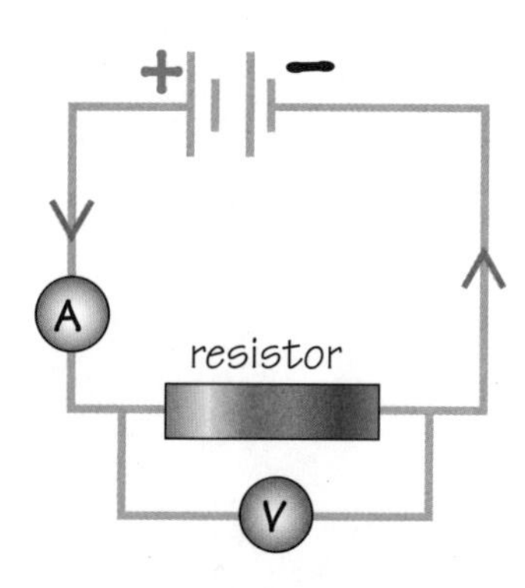

- **Circuit** to measure resistance
  – use variable resistor
  – connect meters correctly
- (A) – ammeter measures current
- (V) – measures potential difference

- **Current-voltage graphs** – show variation of current through a component as voltage varies

- **Ohmic conductor** – **resistance constant** e.g. metal wire at constant temperature

Examiner's tip

Graphs should have a label and unit on each axis

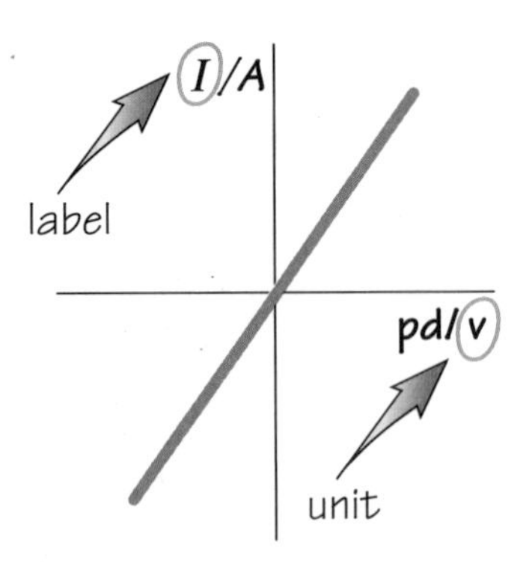

Note that 'I' is the symbol for current. 'A' stands for Amperes (Amps)

- **Non-ohmic conductor** – **resistance varies** e.g. lamp filament – resistance increases with temperature

If temperature rises, energy of metal particles increases. Hence, more frequent collisions with conducting electrons

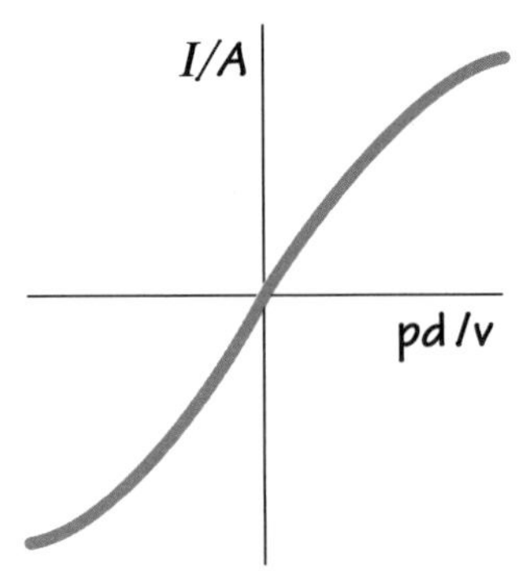

- **Non-ohmic conductor** – current in one direction only – very high resistance in reverse direction e.g. silicon diode for voltage greater than 0.6V

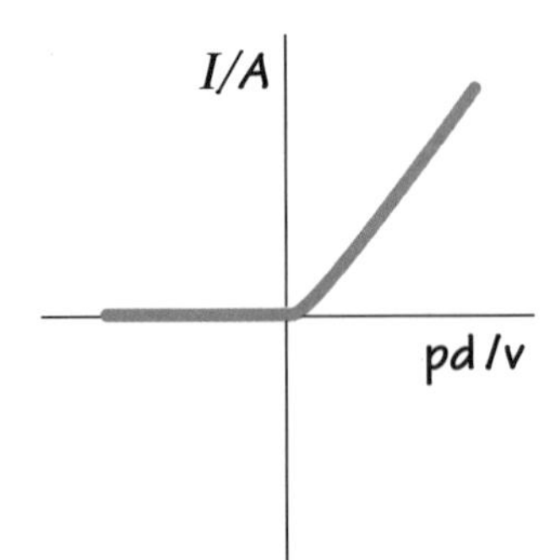

- **Series resistors** $R = R_1 + R_2$

  – current same through resistors
  – potential difference (pd) divided up

If $R_1 = R_2$, $R = R_1/2$ $= R_2/2$

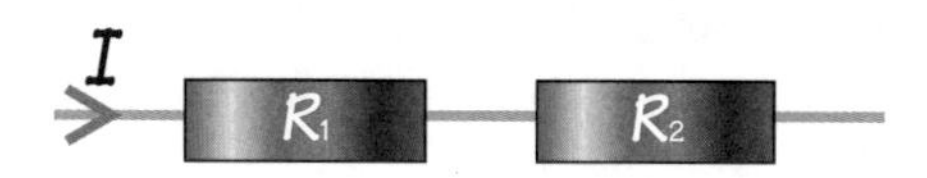

- **Parallel resistors** $\frac{1}{R} = \frac{1}{R_1} + \frac{1}{R_2}$

  – current adds up at junction
  – pd same across resistors

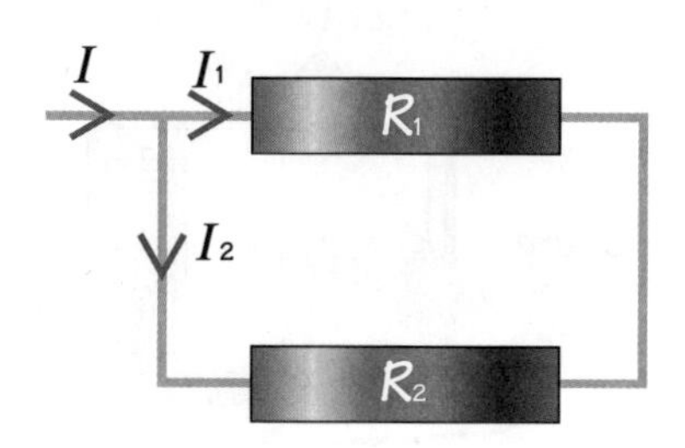

- **Series cells** $V = V_1 + V_2$

V1 V2
\+ - + -

Symbols

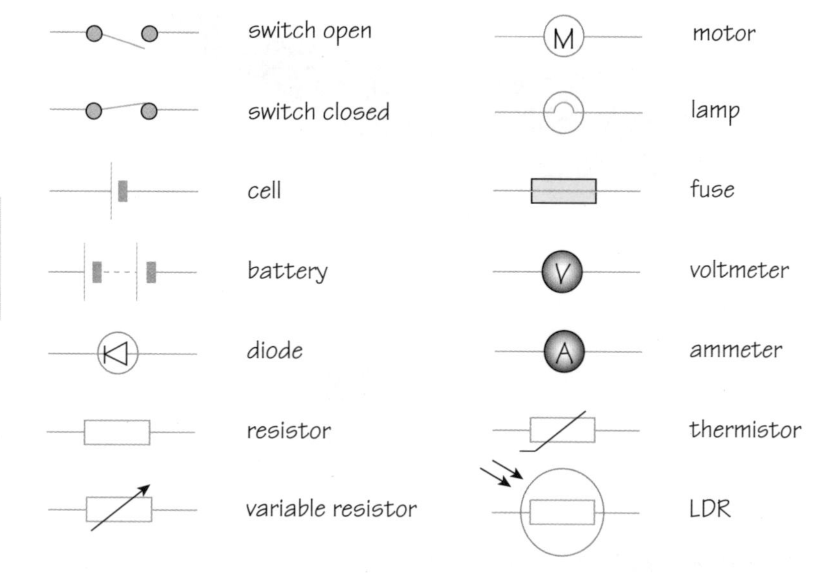

Examiner's tip
Make sure you can interpret and draw circuit diagrams

- **Electrical sources** – solar cells, batteries, cells, generators
- **Electrical energy dissipated** – lamps, resistors, bells, meters, LEDs, buzzers

Using electricity

Energy in circuits

- **Electric current** – flow of charge
- **Energy** – given to each electron by battery/power supply
- **More energy** – (pd) higher
- **1 V** – 1 J per coulomb of charge (C)
- **1 A** – current when 1 C flows/second
- **Energy transfer** – **Power = pd x current**
  = energy transfer/second
- **Unit of power** – 1W = 1J/s

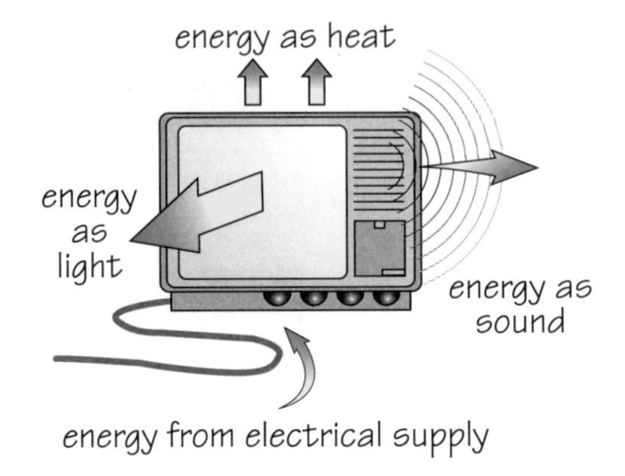

Energy flow through a television

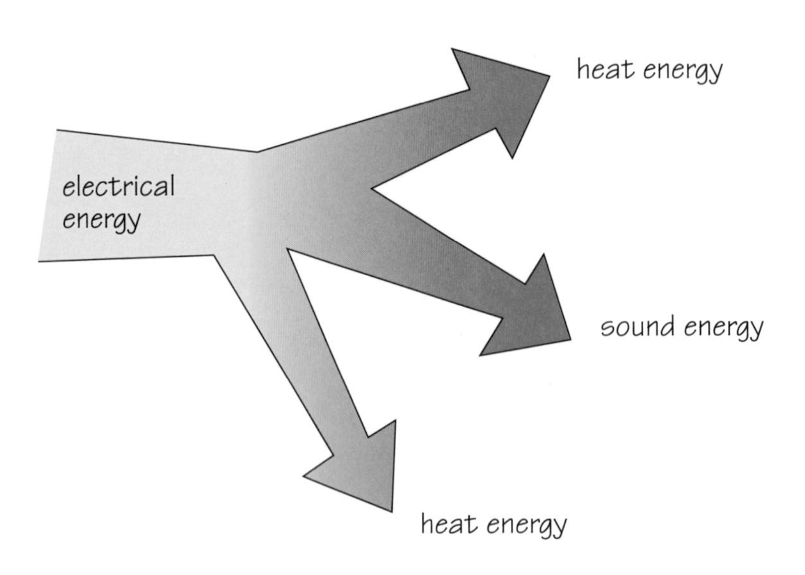

- **Energy transfer = pd x charge**

Note that
charge = current x time

Safety

- **Fuse** – low melting-point wire.
- **Plug** – 3-pin plug needs correct fuse
- **Fuse size** – use I = P/V where P is the power rating in Watts
- **High current** e.g. 12 A – large fuse, 13 A
- **Low current** e.g. 1 A – small fuse, 2 A
- **Circuit breaker** – instead of fuse
- **Metal** case – appliance must be earthed
- **Plastic** case – extra protection
- **Table lamp** – low current
  – often no need for earth
- **Kettle** – high current
  – must have earth

Appliance with plastic case is said to be 'double-insulated'. Symbol on appliance is ⧈

Brown goes on right
blue goes on left

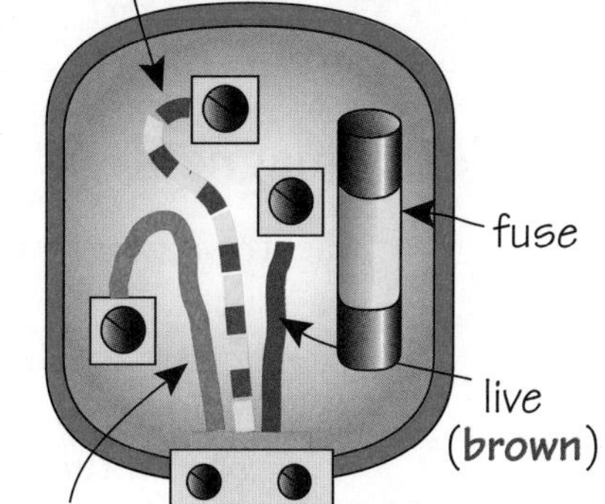

Examiner's tip

There is usually a question on plugs and/or fuses

heating coil

earth point

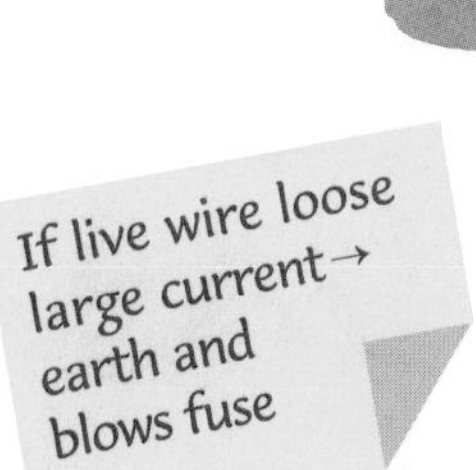

Mains supply

- **UK supply about 230 V ac**

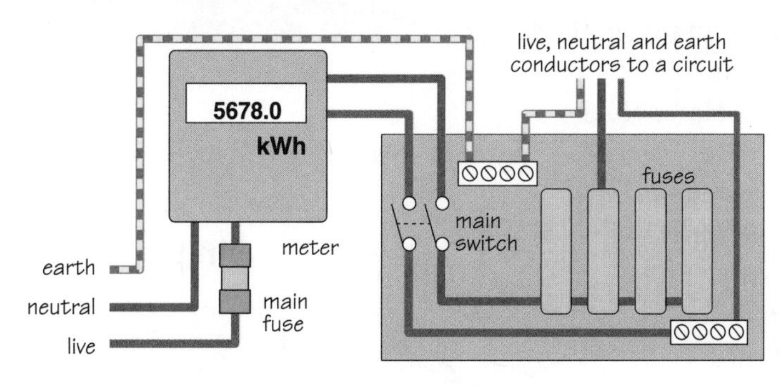

- **Live** wire – energy supplied
- **Neutral** wire – return for current
- **Earth** wire – no current
  – protects user
- **Live terminal** – alternates between +ve and –ve voltage
- **Neutral terminal** – stays near zero voltage
- **Amount of energy transfer depends on** – time appliance switched on
  – power of appliance

Cost

Examiner's tip
You can expect a question to calculate cost

- **Unit** – kilowatt hour (kWh)
- **Kilowatt** – 1000 watts
- Energy transferred = power x time
- **Total cost** – number of units x cost per unit
- **Example** – 3 kW for 3 hours = 9 units
  9 units @ 6p = 54p
  – 1500W for 20 minutes equals 1.5kW for $\frac{1}{3}$ hour = 0.5 units

Remember to convert watts into kilowatts and time into hours!

Electromagnetism

Electromagnets

Note that it behaves like a bar magnet and has a similar magnetic field

- **Electromagnet** – coil of wire with electric current
- **Strength** of an electromagnet increased by
  – placing an iron core in it
  – increasing the number of turns of wire
  – increasing size of current through it
- **Reverse current** – poles reverse

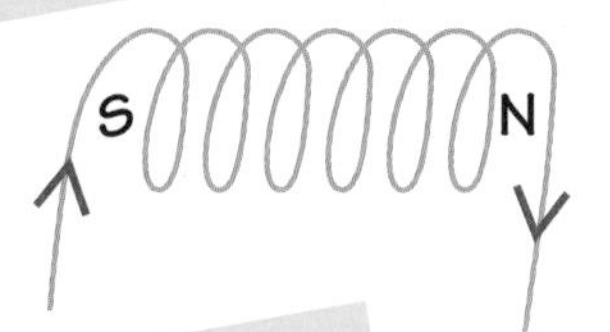

Look at end of coil, direction of current tells you which pole it becomes

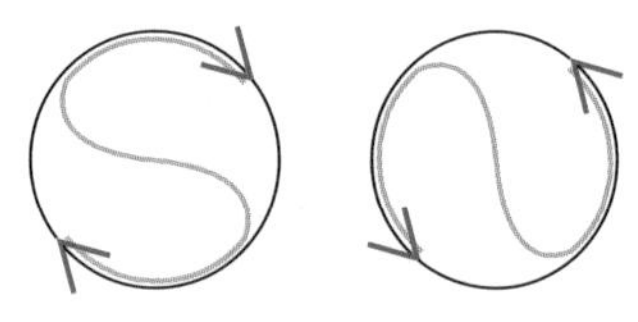

Examiner's tip
You should be able to sketch magnetic field patterns

Electromagnetic forces

- Force on wire in magnetic field
- Direction of force
  – Fleming's Left Hand Rule
  – direction of force reverses if current reverses or magnetic field reverses
- Size of force increases with
  – strength of magnetic field
  – size of current
  – increased number of turns of wire

Simple Motor

force
N
coil
S
Thrust (Thumb)
force
Field (First finger)
Current (Second finger)
-
+
commutator

Note that split-ring commutator reverses current in coil every half turn

Applications
- **Motors** – force produces **rotary movement** e.g. electric drill, washing machine
- **Loudspeakers** – **cone forced in and out** to produce sound waves
- **Circuit breakers** – **high current activates electromagnet**
- **Electric bell** – clapper attracted to bell

Examiner's tip
Examiners often set questions on applications to show an understanding of the principles

Electromagnetic induction

Examiner's tip
You need to be able to explain how an ac generator works

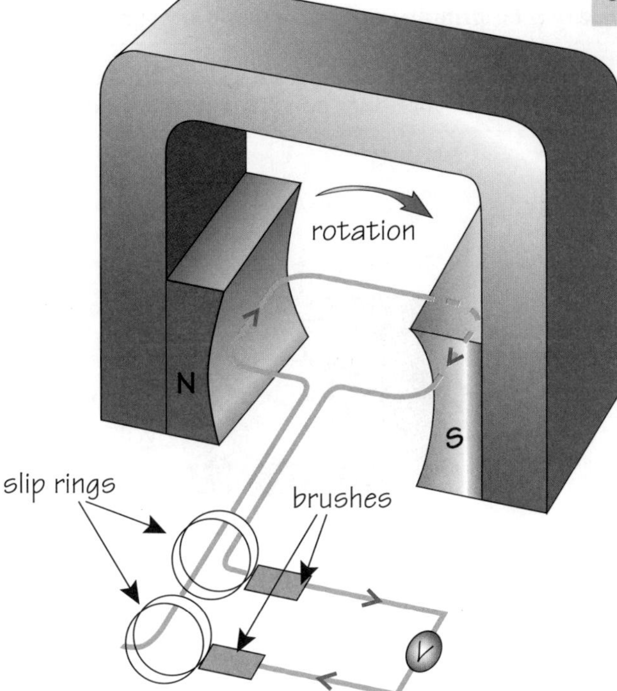

- **Coil cuts** magnetic field – **pd** produced
- **Induced voltage** – **current** flows
- **Size of induced voltage** depends on:
  - **speed** of movement of coil/magnet
  - **strength** of magnetic field
  - **number of turns** on coil
  - **area** of coil

Use the right hand rule to find the direction of the current in a generator

Applications
- **Generator/dynamo** – **produces electricity**
- **Transformers** (see next page) – **change size** of a **voltage**

Alternating current

- **Direct current** (dc) – **electrons move in one direction**
- **Batteries produce dc**
- **Alternating current** (ac) – **electrons change direction**
- **Power stations produce ac**
- **Mains** electricity – **ac** supply
  – **frequency is 50 hertz**

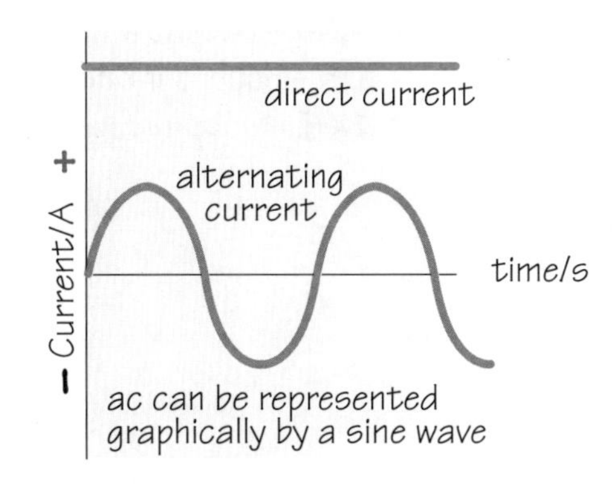

ac can be represented graphically by a sine wave

Transformers

Changing magnetic field induces voltage in transformer

- **High current** – a lot of heat (Power = I^2R)
- **High voltage** – avoid heat loss
- **Power stations** – produce electricity at high voltage
- **Transformers** – step down (or up) voltages
  – work on ac not dc
- **Electricity at home** – 230/240 V ac (in UK)

secondary pd = primary pd x no. secondary turns/no. primary turns

secondary pd x secondary current = primary pd x primary current

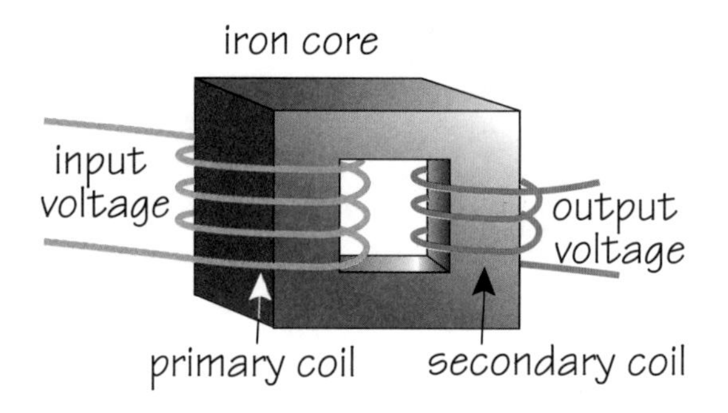

Control in electronic circuits

Electronic systems

- **Input sensors** – detect change e.g. LDRs (light), thermistors (heat)
- **Processor** – decides action needed e.g. logic gates AND, OR, NOT
- **Output devices** – indicate result of action e.g. buzzer

Logic gates

- **Process information**
- **Output current** – too small to operate most output devices
- **Output** – predicted from 'truth table'
- **AND** – output if both inputs high
- **OR** – output if one or both inputs high
- **NOT** – output reversed

Potential divider

- **Series components** – divide up pd
- **Provides correct output**
- $V \text{ out} = V \text{ in} \times \frac{R_2}{R_1 + R_2}$

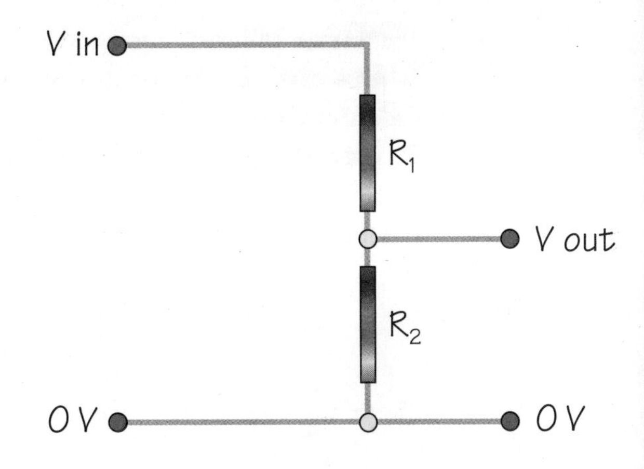

Symbols

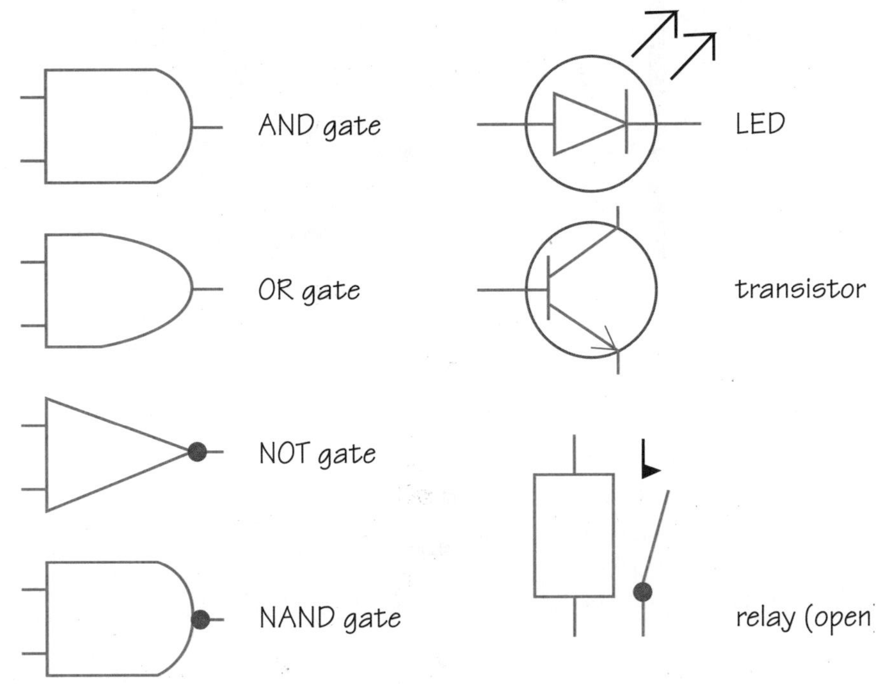

Examiner's tip

You need to be able to recognise these

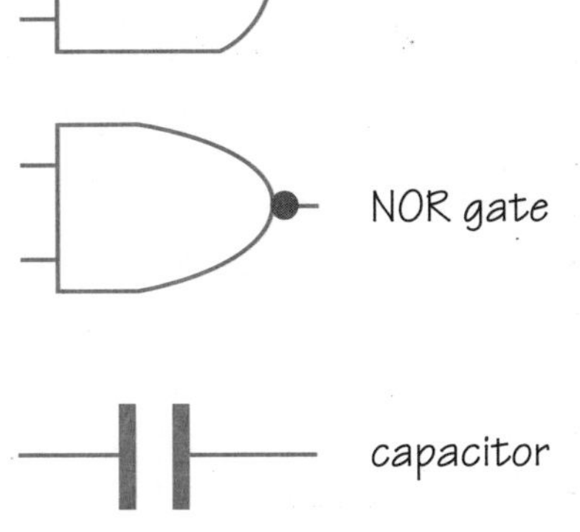

Small current in relay coil can switch circuit where larger current flows

Transistor

Three terminals – base (b)
– collector (c)
– emitter (e)

- **Acts as** – switch
  – **current amplifier**/buffer for high current outputs
- **Switched on** – large enough current to base
- **Switched off** – no/too little current to base

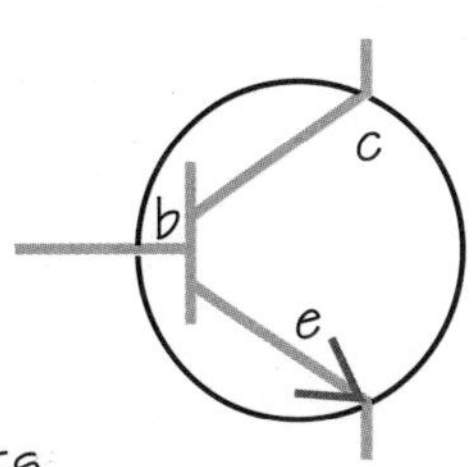

Capacitor

- **Two metal plates** + insulator
- **Stores charge** – connected across power supply
- **Discharges** – conductor connected across it
- **Time to charge/discharge depends on**
  – resistance
  – capacitance

Capacitors are often used as time delay switches in an electronic circuit

Circuits

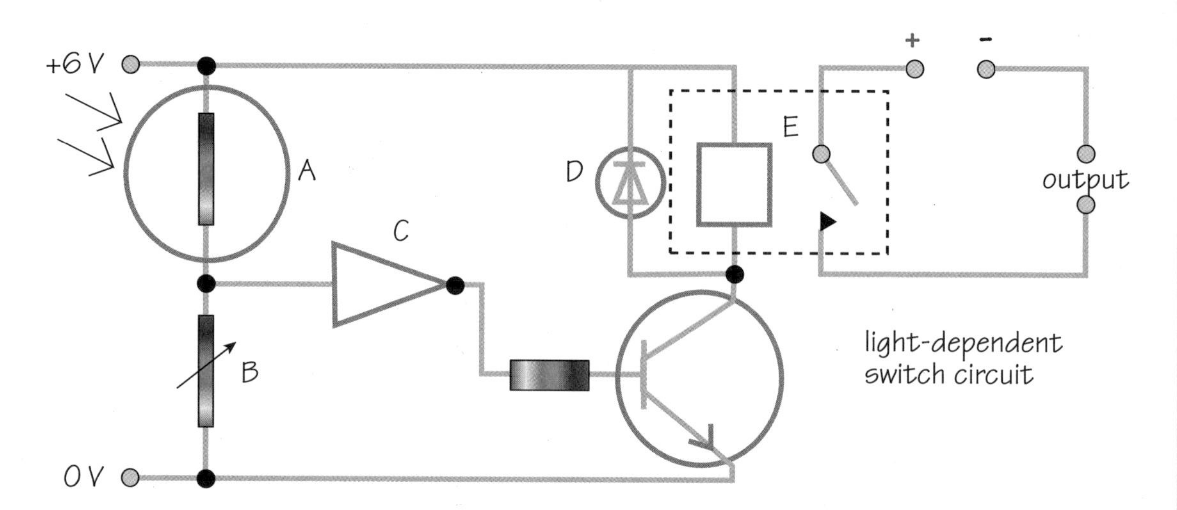

- A – LDR resistance decreases as light level increases (thermistor resistance decreases as temperature rises)
- B – Variable resistor adjusts sensitivity
- C – NOT gate
- D – Diode reverse-biased to protect transistor
- E – Relay

A and B act as input to NOT gate

Latch

- Maintains high output even when input removed
- Bistable latch used in burglar alarm and acts as a memory circuit remembering last input until reset operated
- Can be made from two NOR gates

Questions

1 In terms of charge transfer, describe what happens when you rub a glass rod with a silk cloth. ______________________________

____

2 In this circuit, the two lamps are identical.

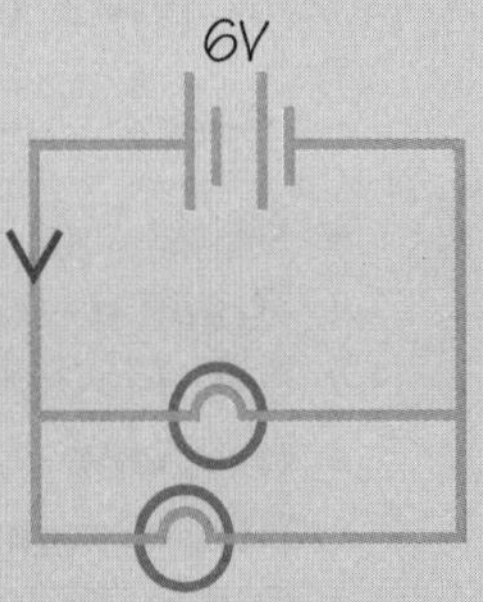

(a) What is the pd across each lamp? ____ V

(b) If the current flow in the main part of the circuit is 3.0 A, calculate the resistance of each lamp filament.

____

____

6V

3 An electric kettle is rated at 1.5 kW.

(a) Assuming that the domestic voltage supply is 250 V, what is the correct-sized fuse for the plug? (Choose from the following sizes: 1 A, 2 A, 3 A, 5 A, 10 A, 13 A) ______________________________

____

(b) A unit of electricity costs 6p. How much does it cost to operate the kettle for 20 minutes a day, each day for a week? ______________________________

____

4 (a) What is meant by a step-up transformer? ______________________________

____

(b) The primary coil of a transformer has 100 turns. An alternating pd of 2.0 V is applied across it. If an output voltage of 7.0 V is needed, how many turns of wire should the secondary coil have? ______________________________

____

5 (a) In this circuit, the resistor, R and the thermistor, T form a 'potential divider'. Explain what this means.

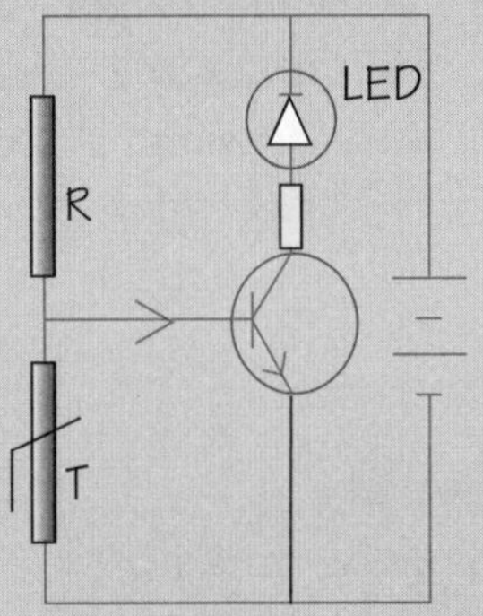

____

____

LED

R

T

(b) The resistance of the thermistor decreases when it gets hotter. What then happens in the rest of the circuit as the thermistor is heated?

____

____

(c) What component could you connect into the base of the transistor to reverse the action of the circuit?

____

Forces and motion

Representing motion

Distance-time graphs

- **Speed = distance/time**
- **Units** – m/s (ms^{-1})
- **Graph *a*** – stationary body
- **Graphs *b* and *c*** – steady speed
- **Gradient** → speed: b faster than c
- **Straight line** – speed constant or zero
- **Curved line** – speed varies
  - gradient of tangent = instantaneous speed
  - (car) speedometer measures instantaneous speed

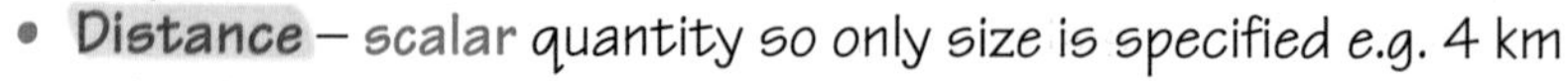

- **Distance** – scalar quantity so only size is specified e.g. 4 km
  - (car) mileometer/odometer measures total distance
  - total distance gives average speed
- **Displacement** – vector quantity so size and direction are specified
  - displacement gives average velocity
  - displacement–time graph for e.g. motion of a lift gives information about direction

Velocity-time graphs

- **Acceleration = change in velocity/time taken**
- **Units** – m/s² (ms^{-2})
- **Graph *a*** – constant velocity
- **Graphs *b* and *c*** – constant acceleration
- **Gradient** → acceleration: b greater acceleration than c
- **Straight line** – acceleration constant or zero
- **Curved line** – acceleration varies
  - gradient of tangent = instantaneous acceleration
- **Area** – distance

Velocity is speed in a given direction

Examiner's tip

Examiners usually set questions on drawing or interpreting graphs

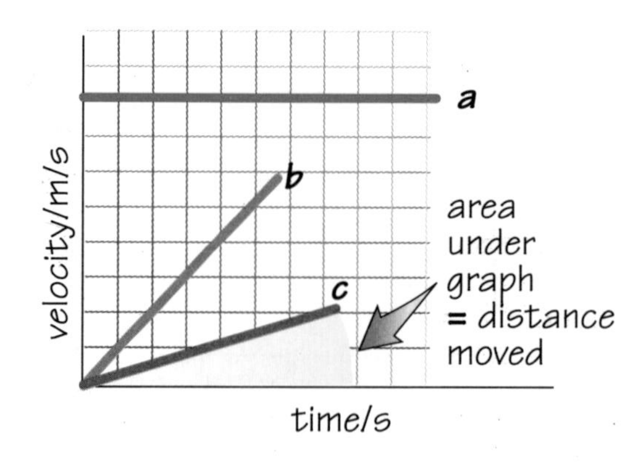

- **Speed–time graph** – no information about direction
- **Velocity–time graph** – gives information about direction
  - – E speeding up opposite direction to A
  - – F constant velocity opposite direction to B
  - – C slowing down

Note that you should be able to measure or calculate the gradient of different types of graph

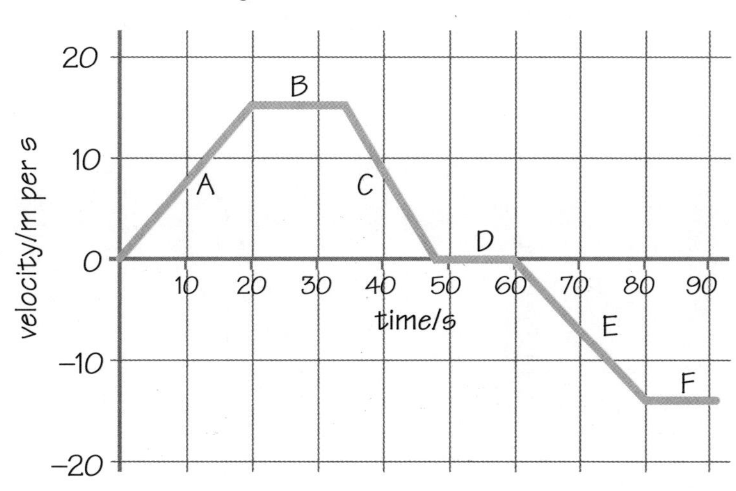

Force-extension graphs

- **Linear part** – F α e (Hooke's Law)
- **OA** – **elastic** region
- **AB** – **plastic** region
- **B** – **yield point**; wire stretches with little load
- **C** – **breaking point**

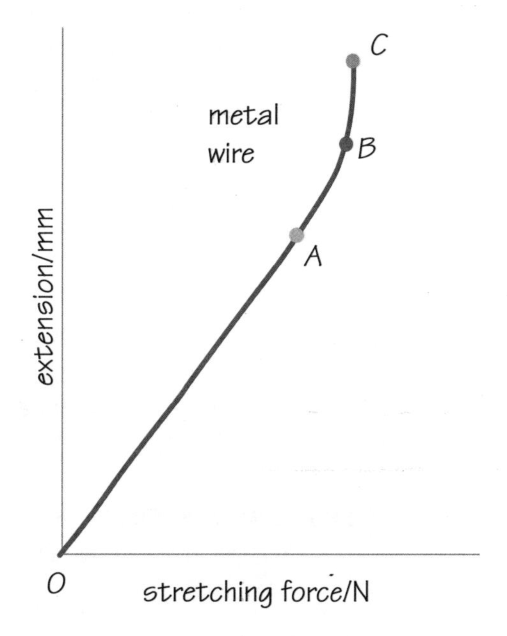

One possible experimental arrangement

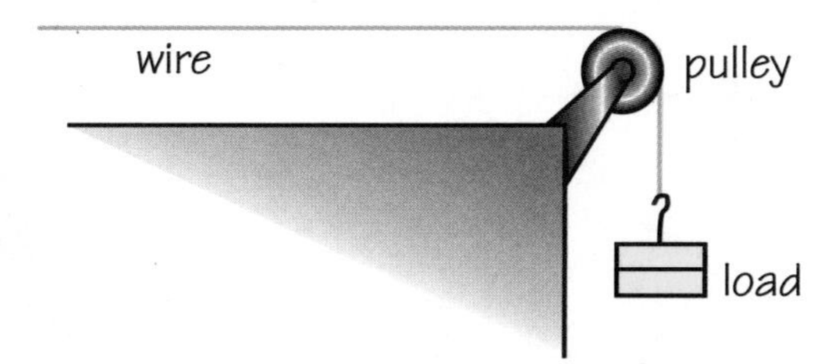

- **Greater force** – greater extension
- **Elastic** – returns to original shape
- **Plastic deformation** – elastic limit exceeded
  - – does not return to original shape

- **Rubber** – does not obey Hooke's law
  – absorbs energy when stretched
- **Slope** – **stiffness** of rubber: smaller slope = stiffer
- **Car tyre** – carbon and rubber
  – stretchy tread/good grip
  – stiff tyre wall does not need to change shape

New tyres use silicon not carbon - less heating when deformed - increases performance/decreases fuel consumption

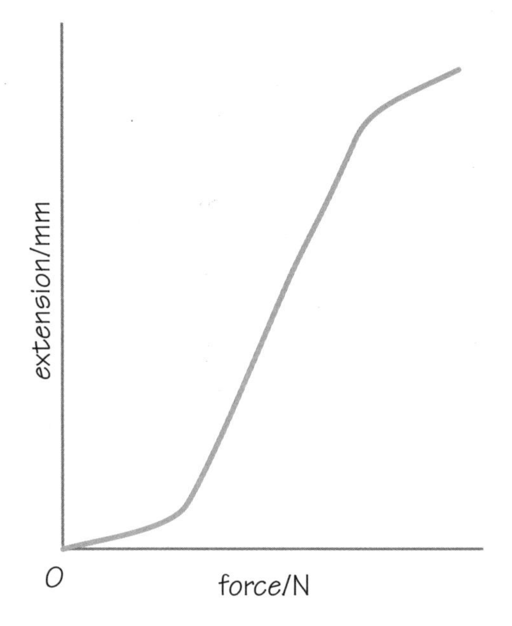

Equations of motion

- $v = u + at$
- $v^2 = u^2 + 2as$
- $s = ut + \frac{1}{2}at^2$
- $s = \frac{1}{2}(u + v)t$

v is final velocity
u is initial velocity
s is displacement
a is acceleration
t is time

Remember that velocity (and displacement) is a vector. Use +value for body falling down and -value for body thrown upwards

- **Negative acceleration** – deceleration
  –g always directed downwards: use +g in equations

Projectiles

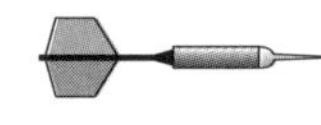

- **Path** – parabola
  – body travels horizontally and falls under gravity
- **Horizontal motion** – **constant speed**
  – use speed = distance/time
- **Vertical motion** – **body falls** from rest
  – use $s = \frac{1}{2}gt^2$

Balanced forces

- **Newton's first law** – object keeps going, or stays still, unless unbalanced force acts
- **Force** – something that changes the way an object moves or stays still
  - can change shape of an object
  - types include elastic, magnetic, gravitational

- **Weight, W** – downwards on table
- **Force, R** – upwards on book
- **R = W** – forces balance
  - book stationary

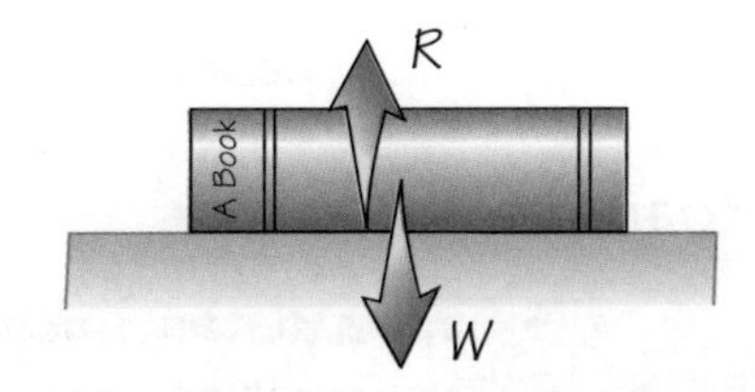

- **Thrust, T** – car pushed through air
- **Force, R** – air drag on car
- **R = T** – forces balance
  - car constant speed

other (frictional) forces also act on the car

- **W greater than R** → book falls!
- **T greater than R** → car accelerates!
- **Forces unbalanced**
- **Unbalanced forces** – change in motion

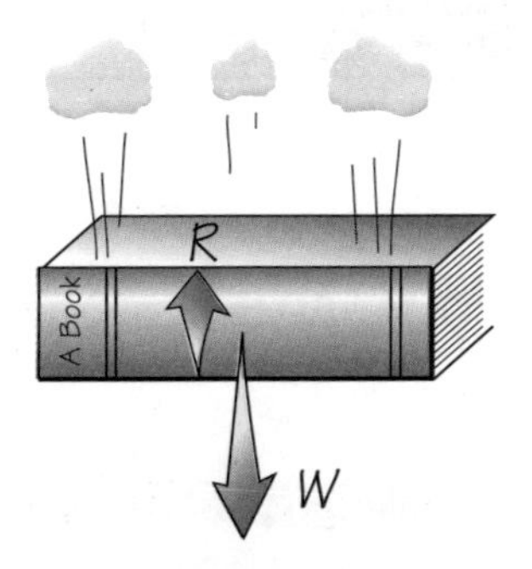

- **Greater force** – greater acceleration
- **Bigger mass** – greater force needed
- **Force = mass x acceleration**
- **Units** – Newtons (N)
- **1 N** – 1 kg m/s^2
- **Crumple zones** – reduce forces in car collision by reducing deceleration
- **Seat belts** – increase time for passengers to stop and reduce force exerted

Note that the force in this equation is the resultant or unbalanced force

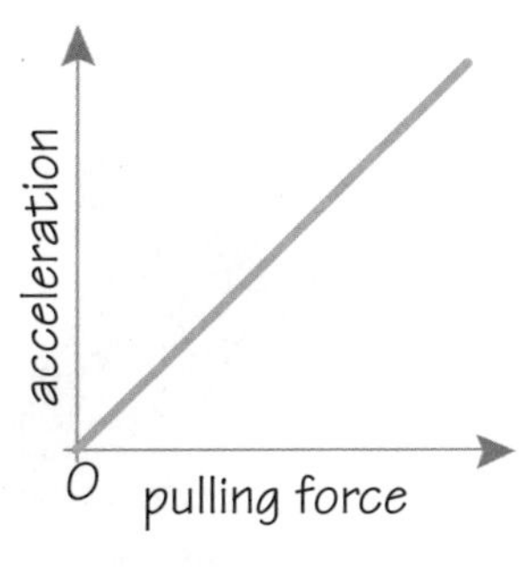

acceleration α force

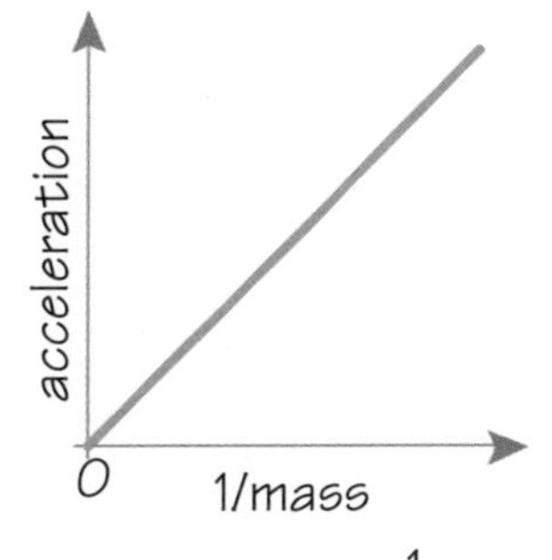

acceleration $\alpha \frac{1}{\text{mass}}$

Friction

- **Friction acts**
  - between two surfaces
  - when body moves through gas or liquid
- **Friction** – opposes motion
  - causes heating/wear e.g. car engine
  - needed for moving and stopping e.g. brakes

Examiner's tip

You need to be able to state or describe where friction is useful and where it is a nuisance

Road safety

- **Stopping distance depends on**
  - driver reaction time
  - braking distance
- **Braking distance depends on**
  - speed
  - tyres
  - brakes
  - road surface

This data is found on back cover of the Highway Code

30 mph

Stopping distance 23 m

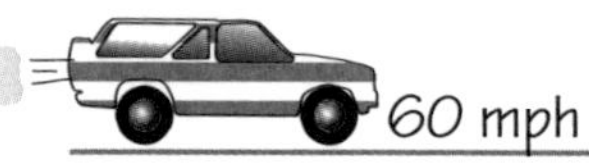
60 mph
Stopping distance 73 m

- **Other factors affecting stopping distance** – poor visibility
  - wet/icy roads
  - poor maintenance of vehicle
- **Braking force too great** – friction may not be great enough
  - skidding may occur

Tyre tread allows tyre to push away water when road wet - tyre stays in contact with road

Free fall

- **Free-falling objects** – same acceleration
  - force of gravity pulls objects down
- **Weight** → acceleration
- **Air drag, R** – increases with speed
- **R = W** → terminal velocity
- **Terminal velocity** – constant velocity
  - zero acceleration
  - about 120 mph in air

acceleration of free fall is about $10 m/s^2$

Turning forces

- **Weight** – windmill turns
- **Turning effect greater if**
  - **weight** (or force) **greater**
  - **distance** to pivot is **greater**
- **Turning effect** = **force** × **perpendicular distance to pivot**
- **Moment** – another name for **turning effect**

- **LH force/s** – turn beam ↶
- **RH force/s** – turn beam ↷

Words clockwise and anticlockwise don't need to appear if symbols ↷ and ↶ do

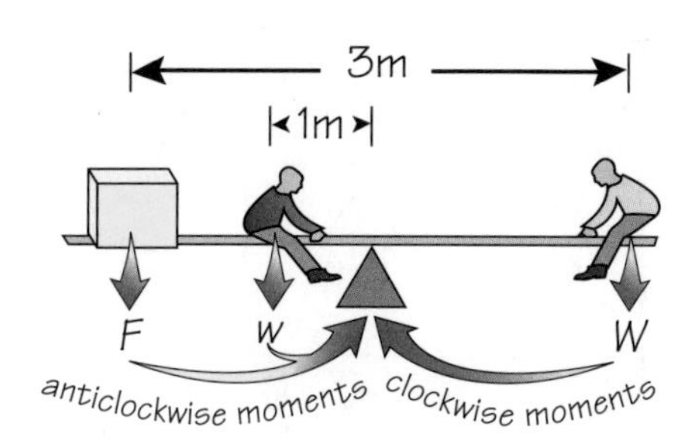

moments = F x 1.5 + W x 1
moments = FW x 1.5

- **Principle of moments**

In equilibrium, Sum ↷ moments = Sum ↶ moments so F x 1.5 + W x 1 = W x 1.5

– apply to different situations e.g. muscles in body, see-saw, machines

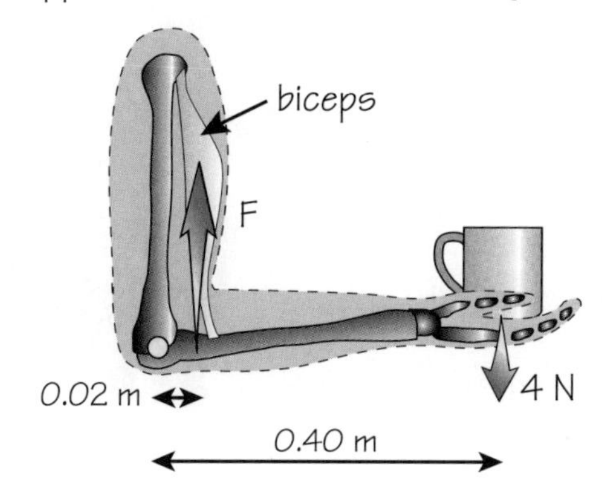

– force F exerted by biceps; moment of F about elbow = moment of weight about elbow

$F \times 0.02 = 4 \times 0.40$
$\therefore F = 1.60/0.02$
$= 80$ N

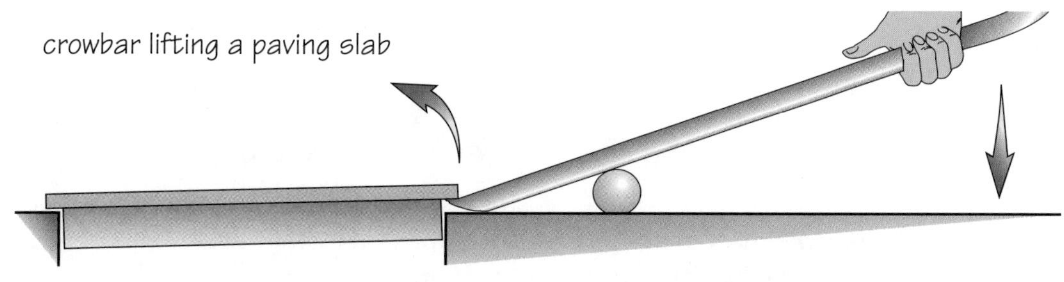
crowbar lifting a paving slab

- **Levers** – use forces to turn things e.g. crowbar
  - **force magnification** where force exerted nearer pivot
  - **distance magnification** where small movement at one end gives larger distance at other end

Centre of mass

- **Weight** – force pulling body towards Earth
- **Centre of mass** – where weight acts
  – where body balances
- **Uniform body** – centre of mass in middle e.g. ruler
- **Non-uniform body** – centre of mass not in middle e.g. snooker cue
  – centre of mass can lie outside body e.g. boomerang
  – centre of mass found by simple experiment with plumb-line

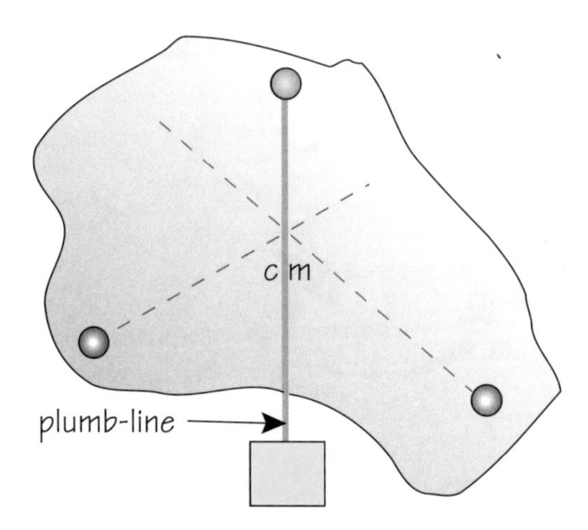

- **Plumb-line** – weight on end of string
- **Suspended object** – centre of mass directly below suspension point
  – suspend from at least two points
  – intersection of lines is centre of mass (cm in above diagram)
- **Symmetrical object** – centre of mass along symmetry axis

Stability

Stability increases if centre of mass is nearer ground e.g. sports car

- **Stable** – weight line inside base
- **Unstable** – falls if pushed
  – weight line outside base
- **Neutral** – centre of mass stays same height

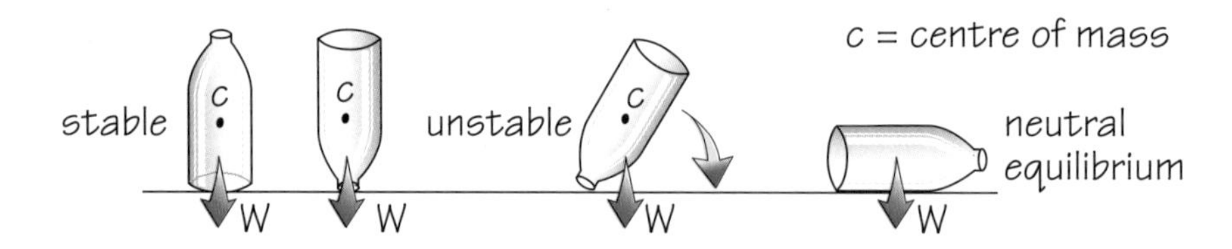

- **Critical point** of stability – centre of mass vertically above edge of base
- **Increased stability** – lower centre of mass
  – base of object wider
- **Centre of mass of human body** – near navel
  – higher for tall people so bigger feet to make stable (advantage for high jump)
  – lower for short people (advantage in sports such as judo where stability important)

Momentum

- **Momentum** – body that is **moving**
- **More momentum** – **harder to stop** moving
- **Momentum depends on** – **mass**
  – **velocity**
- **Momentum = mass x velocity**
- **Units** – **kg m/s**
- **Collision** – objects exert **force**
  – +ve force = –ve force
  → momentum change
  – +ve momentum = –ve momentum

Momentum is a vector - so direction is important

Examiner's tip

Remember to quote correct units in a calculation

- **Conservation** – momentum before = momentum after
  – momentum conserved (no external forces)
- **Kinetic energy** – total kinetic energy after usually less
  – energy lost in heat/sound
  – greater KE lost means collision less elastic
- **Explosion** – conservation of momentum still applies
  – gun fires bullet, momentum of bullet forward = momentum of gun backward, giving recoil velocity of gun

Elastic collision is where there is no loss of KE e.g. atomic collisions

Circular motion

- **Circular path** – **direction changes** → **velocity changes**
  → **acceleration towards centre**
- **Centripetal force** – acts on body since **F = m x a**
  – acts **towards centre**
- **Centripetal force greater if**
  – **mass** of body **greater**
  – **speed** of body **greater**
  – **radius** of circle **smaller**

Planetary orbits are not perfectly circular; they are elliptical

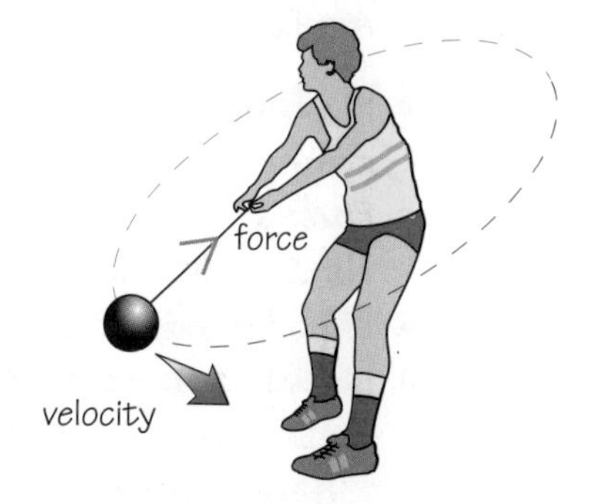

- **Examples** – **planetary motion**/motion of **satellites**
  (gravitational force provides centripetal force)
  – **car rounding a bend**
  (resultant of air resistance and friction provides centripetal force – if corner sharp (radius small), or speed too high or road wet, car will skid because frictional force not big enough)

Pressure

Solids

Example of high pressure

- **Greater force** – greater pressure
- **Greater area** – smaller pressure
- **Pressure = force/area**
- **Units** – N/m^2
- **1 N/m^2** = 1 pascal (Pa)
- Force acts perpendicular to area

Example of low pressure

Applications

- **Sharp knife** – small area
- **Small area** → high pressure
  – other examples: stiletto heel, cutting cheese with wire
- **Snow skis** – large area
- **Large area** → low pressure
  – other examples: camels have large feet, caterpillar tracks on heavy machinery such as bulldozers

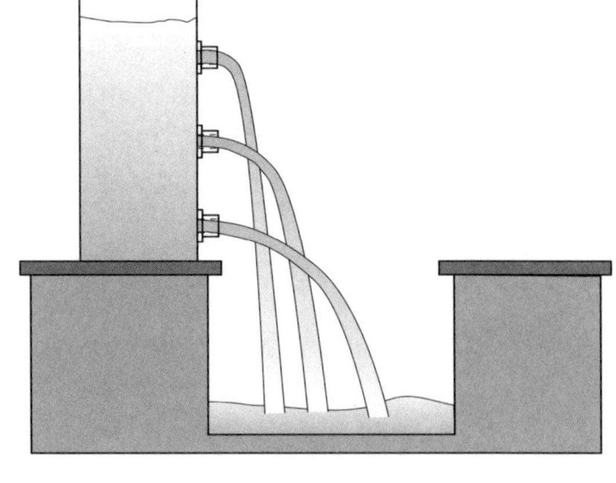

Liquids

- **Pressure increases with depth**
- **Lowest water jet fastest/furthest**
- **Pressure** – equal in all directions

Applications

- **Hydraulic** system – e.g. car jack, car brakes used as force multipliers
- **Forces** – can go round bends/corners
- **No complicated joints** to wear out
- **Liquid used** in brake system – oil
- **Liquids can** – send forces where needed
  – make forces act in required direction
- **Master piston A** – presses on liquid
- **Liquid** – transmits pressure to B
- **Brake piston B** – pressed by liquid
  – has larger area
- **P = F/A** → force α area
- **Force exerted** – larger
  – magnified by ratio of area B/area A

This is the important bit to remember in calculations

A dam is thicker at its base

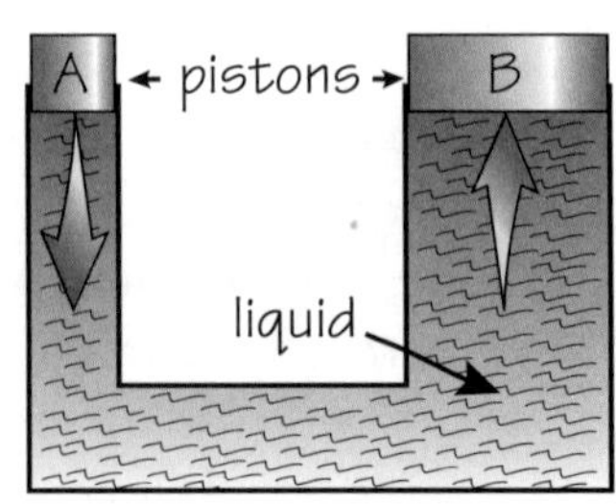

Hydraulic system

Gases

- **Gas particles** – far apart so can easily be pushed closer together
- **Volume decreases** – **increase pressure** (if temperature constant)
  - less space for gas particles
  - particles collide with walls more often

- **Mathematically** – $V \propto 1/p$ → Boyle's Law

This is true for a fixed mass of gas at a constant temperature

- Pressure x volume = constant
- Initial pressure x initial volume = final pressure x final volume
- Pressure/temperature = constant
- **Air exerts pressure** – air pushes down on objects
  - at ground level atmospheric pressure 100,000 N/M^2 or 10^5Pa
  - air inside us exerts equal and opposite pressure
- **Manometer** – can be used to measure gas pressure

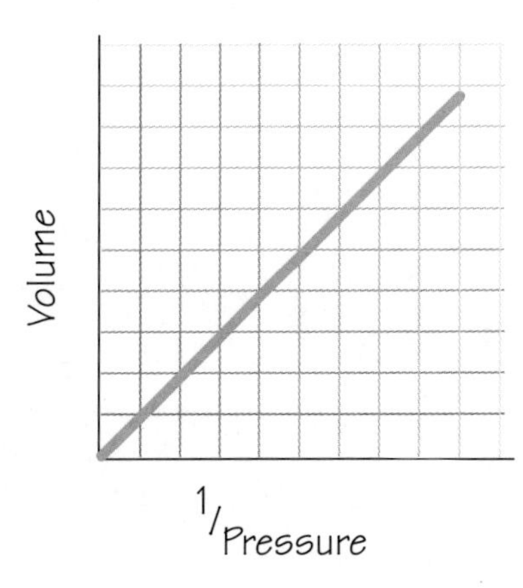

Note that Volume against Pressure is **not** a straight line through origin

Applications

- **Vacuum cleaner** – air pressure inside reduced
  - air pressure outside pushes air and dirt inside
- **Lungs** – diaphragm makes chest volume larger
  - pressure of air reduced
  - air pressure outside forces air into lungs
- **Bicycle pump** – press on piston
  - volume of air decreases
  - air pushed into tyre

Examiner's tip

You should be able to explain gas pressure in terms of particles colliding with container walls

Questions

1 A lorry starts from rest. A velocity-time graph of its motion is drawn for the first 30 seconds.

(a) Describe its motion ______________________

____

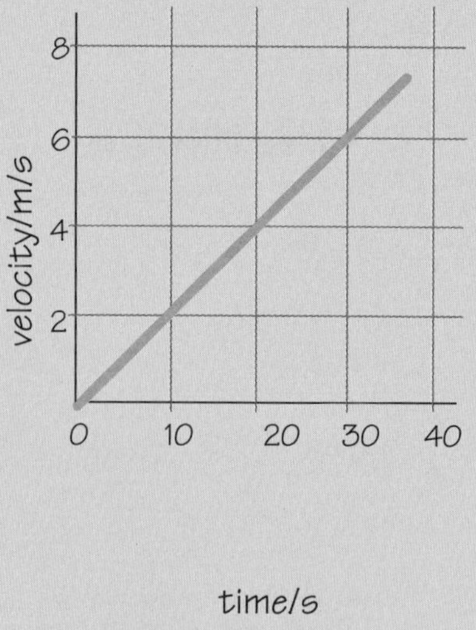

(b) Calculate

i) its acceleration ______________________

____

ii) the distance moved ______________________

____

velocity/m/s

8
6
4
2
0 10 20 30 40

time/s

2 The mass of a sports car is 1200 kg. The engine provides a thrust of 6500 N. Over a measured course, the average air drag is found to be 850 N.

(a) What acceleration is produced? ______________________

____

(b) What does the total stopping distance depend upon? ______________________

____

3 A uniform beam of length 2.5 m is used to weigh sacks of flour. A weight of 120 N has to be placed at point X for it to balance. X is 0.5 m from the pivot. What is the weight of the flour? ______________________

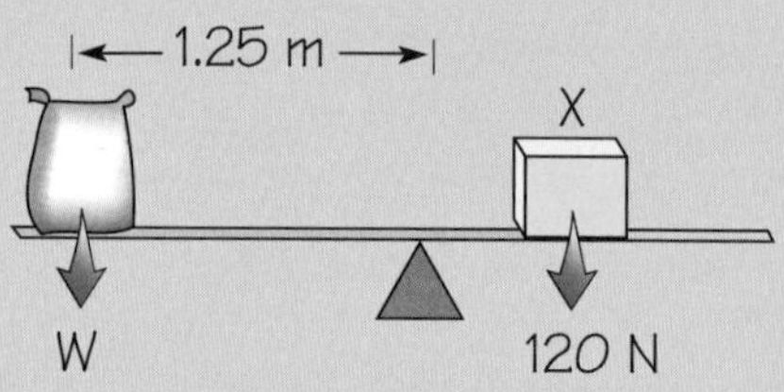

____

1.25 m
X
W
120 N

4 Bus A of mass 5000 kg is travelling east at 10 m/s. At the same time, bus B of mass 3000 kg is travelling in the same direction at 5 m/s. When they collide A and B move together as one. At what speed will they continue to move?

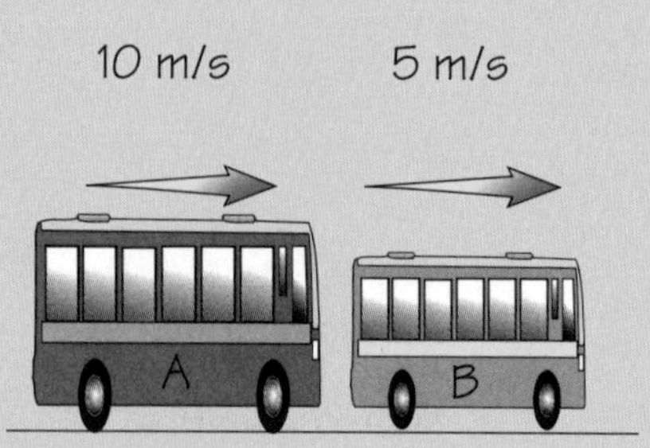

10 m/s
5 m/s
A
B

____

____

____

5 In a car brake system, the brake pedal pushes on a master piston of area 0.1 m^2 with a force of 150 N. If the brake piston is of area 0.4 m^2, what force is exerted on the wheels to stop them?

____

____

Waves

- **Waves transfer energy** not matter

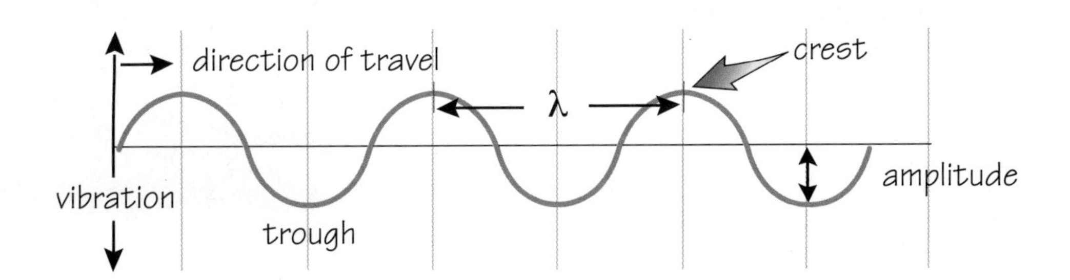

Transverse waves

- **Examples** – water, light, radio
- **Vibration** – 90° to direction of travel
- **Wavelength (λ)** – from one crest to the next
- **Frequency** – number of waves per second; 1 Hz = 1 wave/sec
- **Electromagnetic waves** e.g. light can travel in a vacuum

Period, T = time for one oscillation or cycle.
$$\text{Frequency} = \frac{1}{\text{period}}$$

Longitudinal wave

- **Examples** – sound, slinky spring as diagram below
- **Vibration** – same direction as travel
- **Wavelength** – from one compression to the next
- **Sound travels in solids, liquids, gases but not a vacuum**

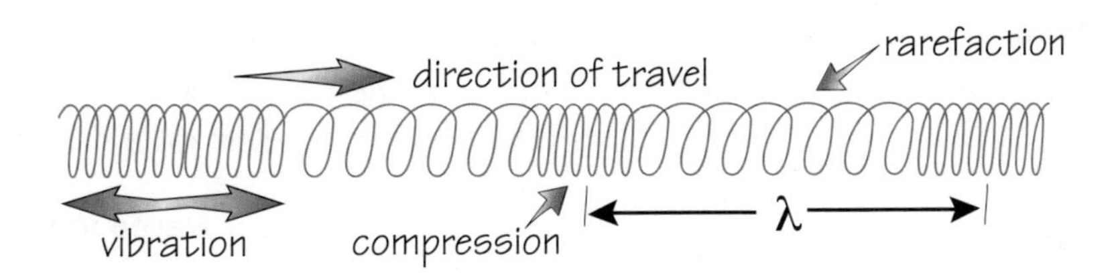

- **Wavespeed = wavelength × frequency** ; $v = \lambda \times f$

This equation applies to **all** waves

Properties of waves

Reflection

- **Angle i = angle r for all waves**
- **Mirror image** – virtual
  – same size
  – upright
  – OM = MI

A quick way to draw this accurately:
1) draw object + 2 incident rays
2) since OM = MI, draw in image
3) draw dotted lines joining incident rays to image
4) extend dotted lines as rays on LH side of mirror

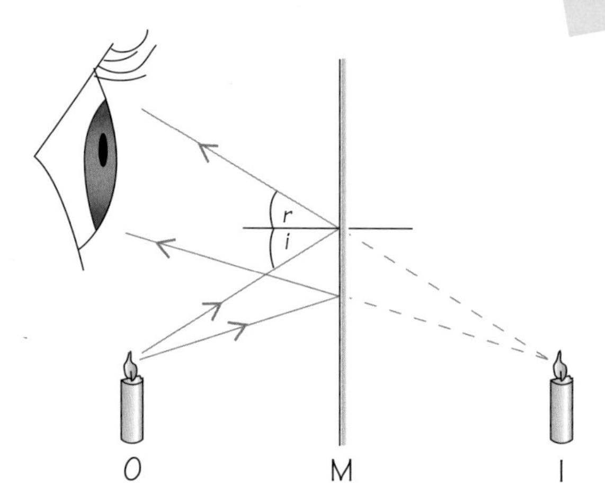

Examiner's tip

Remember arrows on diagram show direction of the light

- **All waves** can be reflected
- **Diffuse reflection** – surface rough e.g. paper
  – reflected light scattered
- **Regular reflection** – smooth surface e.g. mirror
  – reflected light in same direction
  – can form image
- **Shape of mirror** – plane (flat) forms same size image
  – convex forms smaller image e.g. car rear view mirror
  – concave forms larger image e.g. dentist's mirror

Refraction

- **Wave passing from one substance to another**
  – Change in speed
  – Water-waves slower in shallow region
  – Water-waves speed up on exit
  – Frequency of waves constant
  – Wavelength changes
- **Direction** – unless along normal means direction changes

Water waves in ripple tank

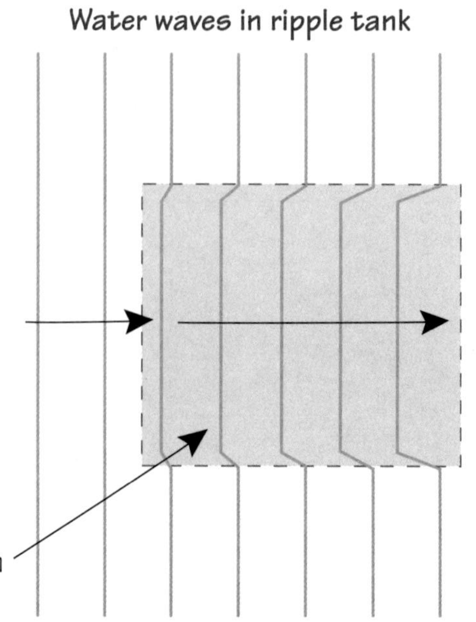

- **Direction at A** – towards normal } see diagram below. Normal is line drawn
- **Direction at B** – away from normal } at 90° to surface
- **Denser medium** – greater refraction
- **Refractive index** – measure of refraction

$$= \frac{\text{speed of light in vacuum}}{\text{speed of light in material}}$$

= about 1.5 for glass

- **Example** – bottom of swimming pool appears nearer; light reflected from bottom changes direction when emerging from water surface so virtual image of bottom seen by observer is above real bottom
- **Sounds, like other waves, can also refract**

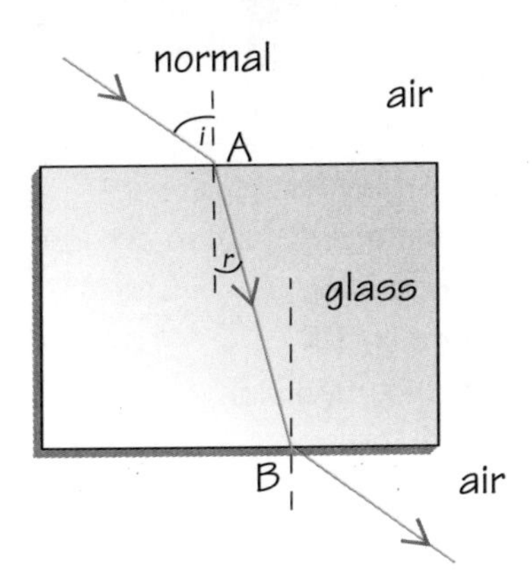

Emergent ray is parallel to incident ray

Total internal reflection

- **Some light** at A (and B) **reflected**
- Small angles of incidence – weak reflection, most refracted
- Larger angles of incidence – stronger reflection, less refraction

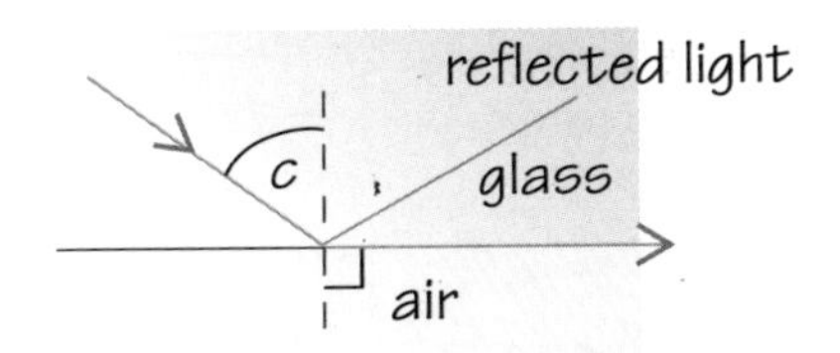

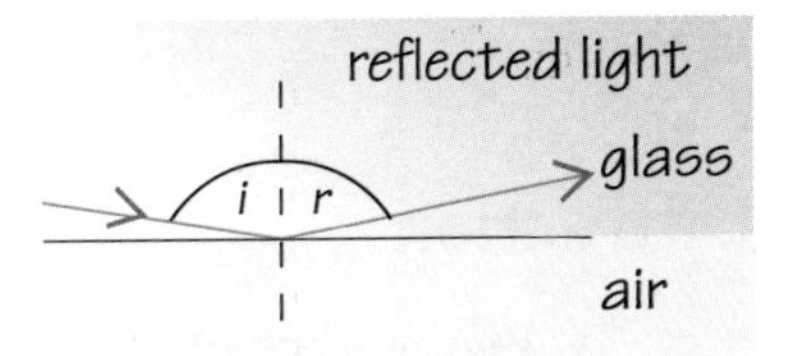

- **Critical angle** – light refracted at 90°
- **Incident angle greater** – all light reflected back
- This is called total internal reflection (TIR)

Note that this only occurs when moving from more dense to less dense

Applications

- **Prisms** – 45° right angle used for periscopes, binoculars, bicycle reflectors
  – light undergoes two internal reflections
  – light turned through 180°

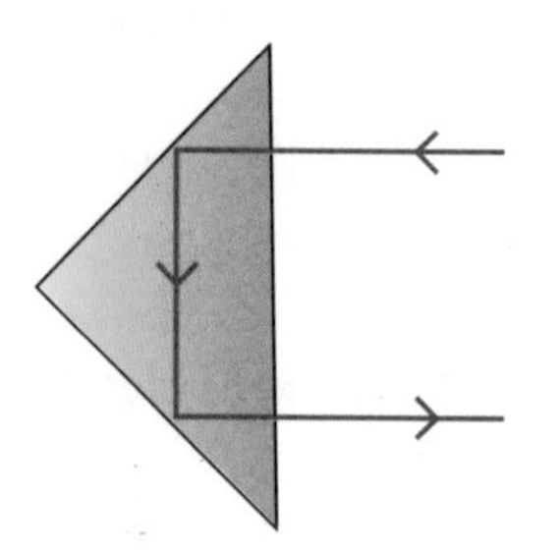

This is because the critical angle for glass is about 42°. The incident angle is 45°

- **Optical fibres**
  – very thin fibre of glass/plastic
  – light hits walls at angle greater than critical angle
  – light reflected back into fibre
  – light travels down fibre by TIR
  – used in communications, medicine

Examiner's tip

You need to be able to describe uses of TIR

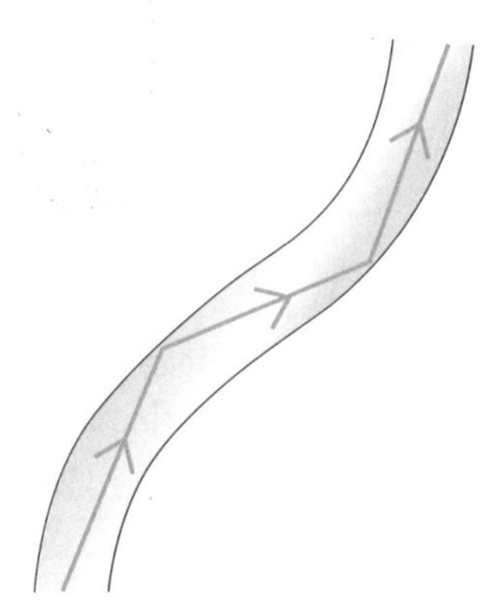

Diffraction

- **Waves spread out** – past obstacle/through gap

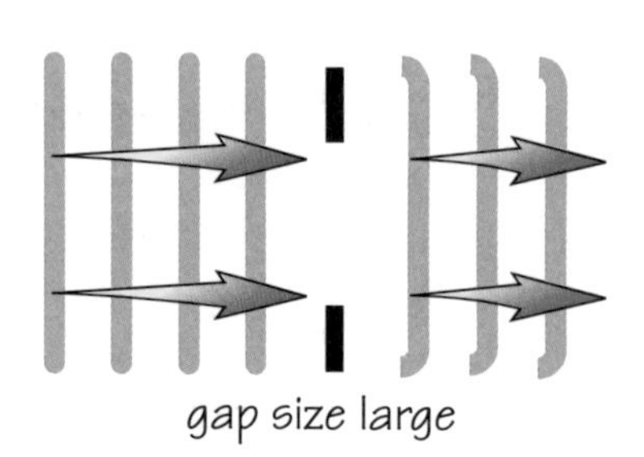

gap size large

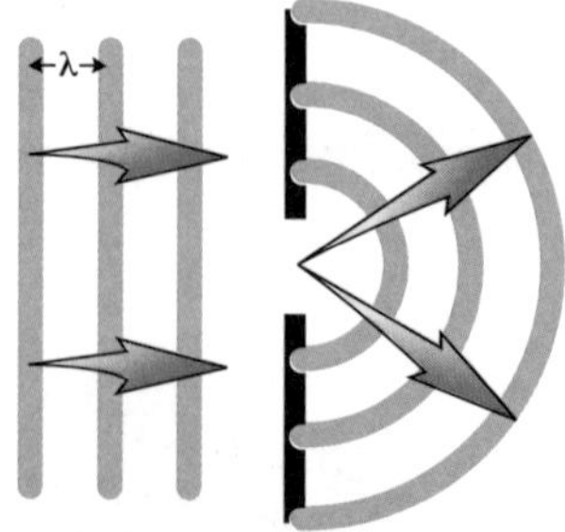

gap same size as wavelength

- **Gap size** – about same as wavelength for maximum diffraction
- **Examples** – sound heard around corners
  – radio signals received in shadow of hills

Light diffraction only observed for very small gap because wavelength is very small

Interference

- **Waves from two sources meet** – if waves same frequency and in step
- **Constructive interference** – crests (or troughs) meet, result is larger displacement e.g. louder sound, brighter light
- **Destructive interference** – crest meets trough, result is smaller displacement e.g. softer sound, darkness

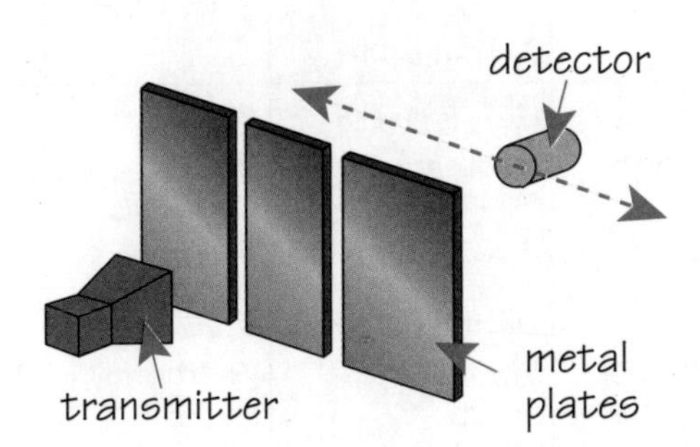

Practical demonstration of the interference of microwaves

- **Path difference** – difference in distance of waves from wave sources
  – whole number of wavelengths means constructive interference
  – odd number of half-wavelengths means destructive interference e.g. $\lambda/2$, $3\lambda/2$

the path difference here is half a wavelength giving destructive interference

the path difference here is one wavelength giving constructive interference

Electromagnetic spectrum

wavelength decreases →   ← frequency decreases

	Radio	Infra-red	Light	Ultra-violet	X-rays	Gamma-rays
Source	Vibrating electrons	Sun, Hot bodies	Sun, Luminous objects	Sun, Mercury, Vapour lamp	Stars, X-ray tube	Radioactive substances, Nuclear reactions
Detector	Radio aerial	Skin, IR photographic film	Eye, Photographic film	Skin (tanning), Photographic film	Photographic film, Electronic detector	GM tube Photographic film
Uses	Communications, Cooking (Microwaves), Astronomy	Heating, Astronomy, Remote control	Seeing, Photography, Photosynthesis	Security marking, Fluorescent lamps	Radiography, Astronomy	Cancer treatment, Radiography

A mnemonic such as **R**eading **I**s **L**ousy **U**nless **E**xtremely **G**ood will help to remember the order

- **Family of waves**
- **Speed** – same = 3×10^8 ms^{-1}
- **Different wavelengths** – reflected, refracted, absorbed, transmitted differently by different substances/surfaces
- **Radiation absorbed** – absorbing substance hotter
  – may produce ac at same frequency as radiation

Radio waves

- **Transmit** – radio/TV over Earth's surface
- **Longer wavelength** – reflected from ionosphere (electrically charged layer in upper atmosphere)
  – enables communication despite curvature of Earth's surface
- **Shorter wavelength** – can penetrate ionosphere
  – used for communication with satellites
  – water molecules can strongly absorb one particular frequency so used for cooking

Known as **microwaves**

Infra-red

- **Readily absorbed** – by rough, **black** surfaces
- **Strongly reflected** – by polished, **light** surfaces
- **Uses** – grills, toasters, radiant heaters, optical fibre communication, remote control of TV/VCR

Examiner's tip

Students often do not show the red and violet rays spreading out from point A

Light

- **Used in optical fibres** – medical endoscopes to see inside patient's body
- **White light** – split into **colours** by prism
- **Spectrum** – **colour depends on wavelength**
- **Most refracted** – **violet**
- **Least refracted** – **red**
- **Brightness** – **depends on intensity/amplitude** of wave
- **Colour filters** – **absorb** different **wavelengths** (colour subtraction)
- **Coloured objects** – behave **like** colour **filters**

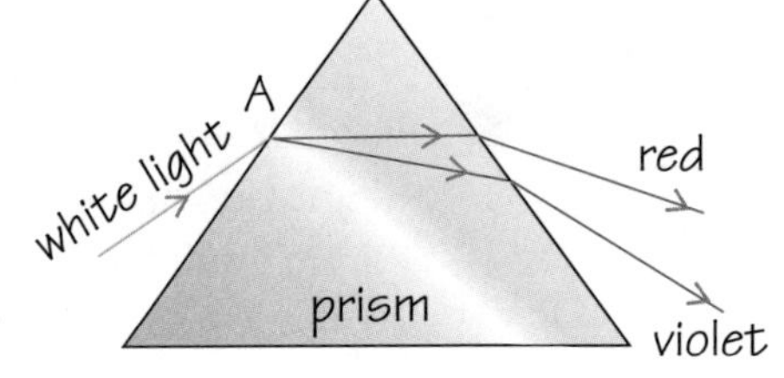

Ultra-violet

- **Uses** – sunbeds/fluorescent lamps/security coding where special coating absorbs radiation and emits light

X-radiation

- **Does not easily pass through bone/metal**
- **Used to produce shadow pictures** of people/materials

Gamma radiation

- **Kills harmful bacteria** in food
- **Sterilises** surgical instruments
- **Kills cancer cells**

Effect on living cells

- **Microwaves** – absorbed by water in cells
  – cells may be damaged/killed by heat released
- **Infra-red** – absorbed by skin
  – felt as heat
- **Ultra-violet** – can pass through skin to deep tissue
  – darker skin absorbs more so less reaches deep tissue
- **X-rays/Gamma rays** – pass through soft tissue
  – some absorbed by cells

Note that **high doses** of UV/X-rays/Gamma **can kill** normal cells, **lower doses** can cause cancer

Optical devices

Eye

- **Cornea** – light enters
- **Cornea/lens** – focus image
- **Retina** – sensitive to light
  – image formed
  – sends image information to brain via optic nerve
- **Perfect eye** – light focused on retina
- **Ciliary muscles** – control lens shape
  – lens thicker, near objects focused
  – lens thinner, distant objects focused
- **Iris** – controls pupil size
  – light dimmer, pupil larger
  – light brighter, pupil smaller

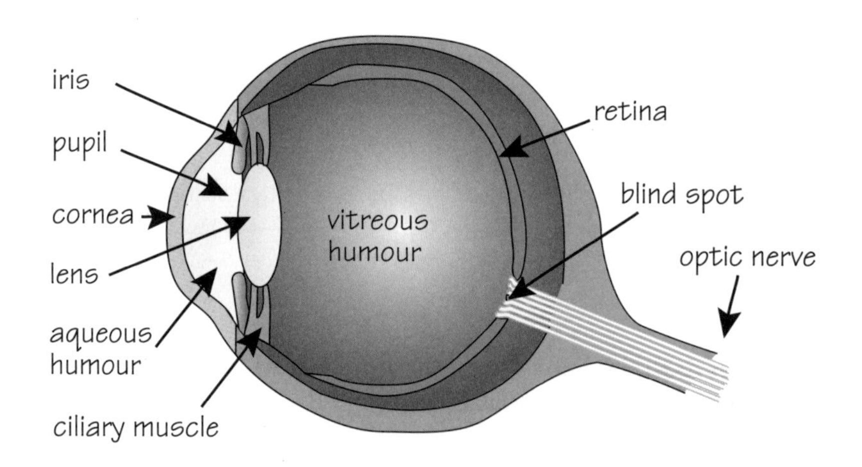

Eye defects

- **Clouded cornea** – replace with clear plastic
- **Short sight** – eye too long/lens too thick
  – correct with concave lens
- **Long sight** – eye too short/lens too thin
  – correct with convex lens

The eye is similar in many ways to a simple camera. Image formed is real, smaller, inverted

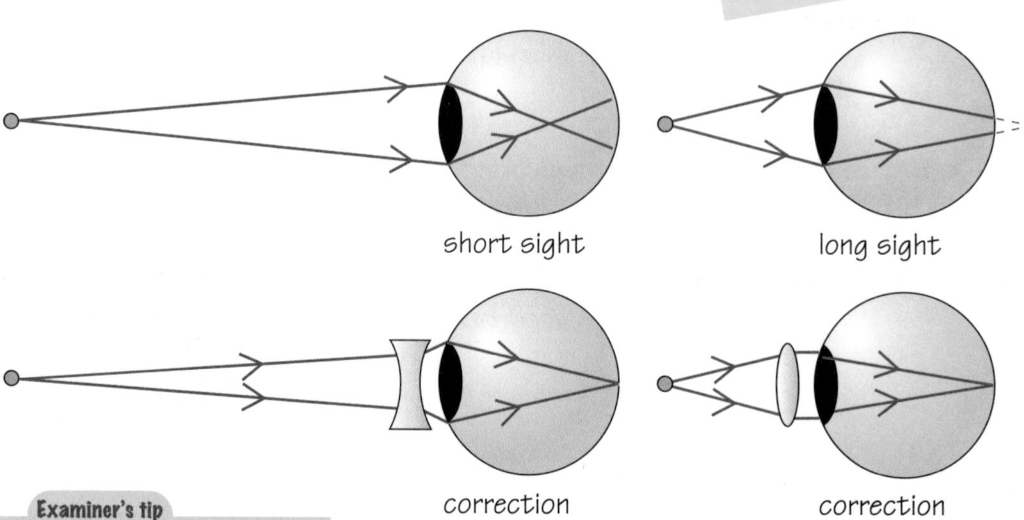

Examiner's tip

Questions are often set on eye defects

Magnifying glass

- **Converging lens**
- **Object** – nearer to lens than focus
- **Image** – magnified
  - upright
  - vertical

Note that you also need to be able to draw a similar diagram to show formation of **real** image by converging lens

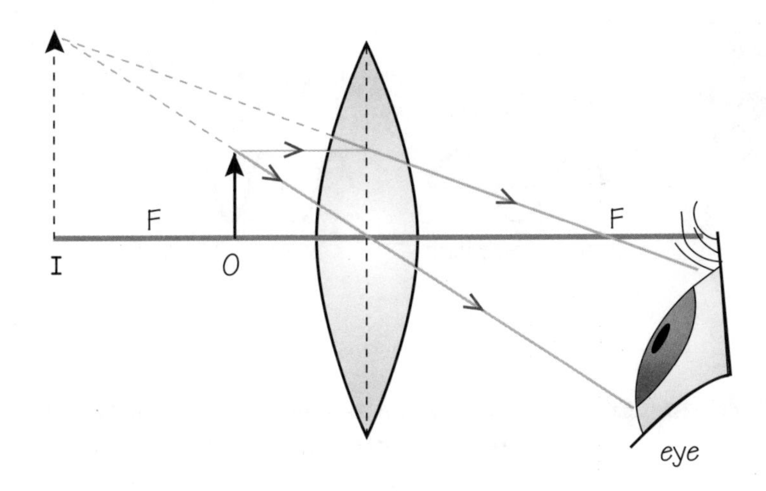

Camera

- **Converging lens** – focuses image
- **Image** – formed on film
  - smaller, inverted, real
  - nearer to lens than object
- **Iris diaphragm** – like iris in eye
  - controls amount of light let in

Distant object - image at focus

Projector

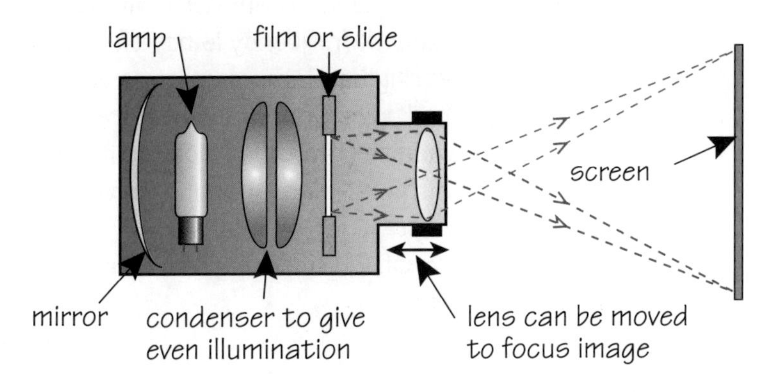

- **Like camera** but in reverse
- **Converging lens** – image of slide/film on screen
- **Image** – larger, upright, real
  - further from lens than slide/film

Sound

- **Vibrations** – produce sound
- **Loudness** – greater amplitude, louder sound
- **Pitch** – higher frequency, higher pitch

A loudspeaker produces sounds by its vibrating cone; bigger movement = louder; faster movement = higher pitch

Examiner's tip

Be prepared to compare oscilloscope traces

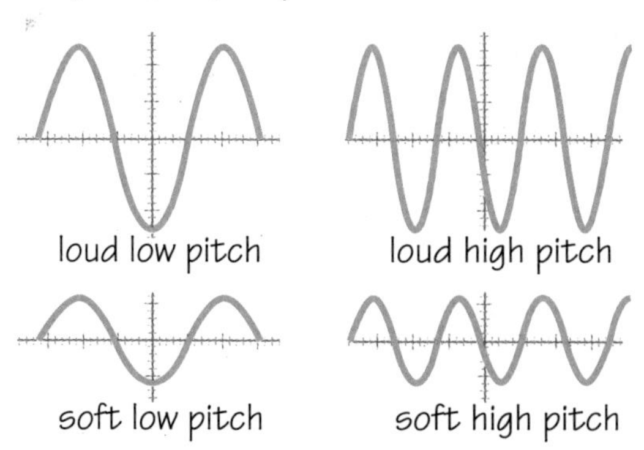

Resonance

- **Natural frequency** – all **objects** have characteristic vibration
  – **depends on size** and **mass** of object
- **Resonance** – object can be forced to vibrate by another vibrating object e.g. tuning fork on bench makes bench vibrate
  – if **forced vibration same as natural frequency** of object, amplitude of vibrations is large
- **Wind instruments** – column of **air vibrates**
  – as length of air column increases, frequency decreases
  – loud sound when air column vibrates at its natural frequency
- **Stringed instruments** – **string vibrates**
  – natural frequency greater if vibrating length is smaller or string thinner or string in greater tension
  – string able to vibrate in different ways or modes; natural frequency is not the only frequency where string has large amplitude: also whole number multiples of fundamental frequency called harmonics
  – quality (timbre) of sound different if string plucked in different places; string vibrates in several modes at once
  – 3f, 5f, 7f – if string of natural frequency f plucked in middle

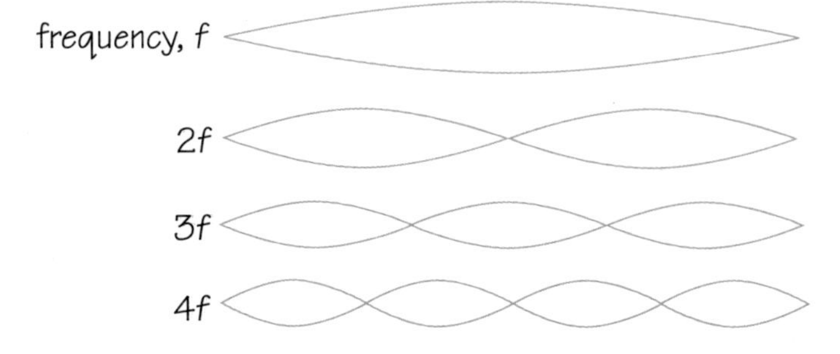

Ultrasound

- **Production** – **electronic systems** can generate **electrical oscillations**
  – oscillations used to generate **sound waves** at **high frequency**
  – ultrasound has frequency **higher** than upper limit of human hearing range – above 20 kHz
- **Reflection** – at boundary between media
  – time for detection gives distance
- **Bats** – detect objects from echoes
- **Sea** – measure depth
  – detect fish shoals
- **Industry** – cleaning delicate objects
  – detect flaws in metal casings
- **Hospital** – pre-natal scanning

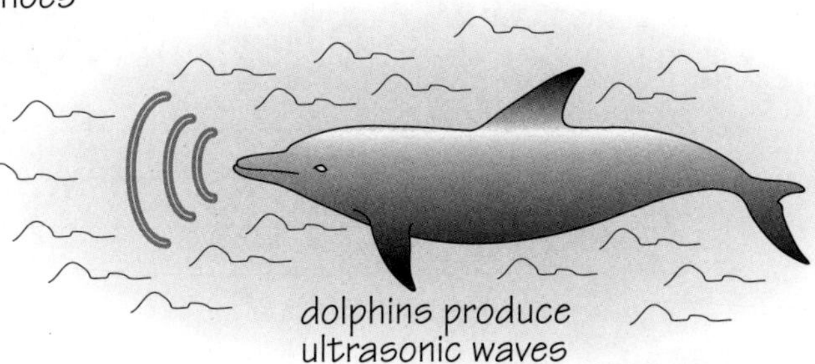
dolphins produce ultrasonic waves

Examiner's tip

Ultrasonic scanning is thought to be safer than using X-rays; state this as a main advantage in an answer

Seismic waves

- **P waves** – longitudinal
  – fast
  – travel through solids, liquids
- **S waves** – transverse
  – slower
  – only travel through solids
- **Refraction** – at boundary between media
  – indicates changing density

Observations suggest Earth – made of layers

Remember that P comes **before** S in the alphabet; P waves arrive **before** S waves

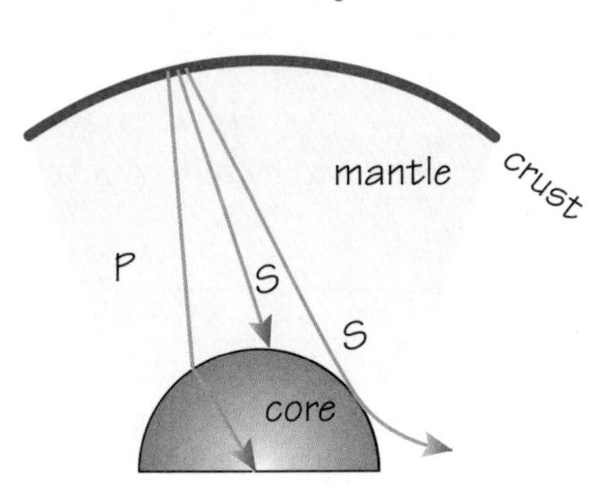

– has **thin crust**
– has **solid mantle** with density increasing with depth
– has **core** just over **half Earth's diameter**
– has **core** with **liquid outer** and **solid inner** part

S-waves cannot pass through liquid outer core

Questions

1 Here is a waveform.

(a) Measure i) its wavelength __________ cm
ii) its amplitude __________ cm

(b) It takes 0.01 s for this waveform to travel across the screen of an oscilloscope.
Calculate
i) its frequency ______________________________
____
ii) its speed ______________________________
____

2 (a) Copy and complete the diagram to show how an image is formed in a plane mirror.

(b) Is the image 'real' or 'virtual'? Explain your answer.
____

3 Echo location techniques can be used by a fishing trawler to find shoals of fish in the sea.
(a) Describe how this works. ______________________________
____

(b) If the speed of sound in water is 1550 m/s and it takes 0.3 s for an echo to be received, how deep is the shoal? ______________________________
____

4 Name two differences between P and S waves sent out from the epicentre of an earthquake.
i) ______________________________
ii) ______________________________

The Earth and beyond

The Solar System

Satellites

- **Moon** – **natural satellite** of Earth
- **Sputnik** – example of **artificial satellite**
  – USSR 1957
- **High orbit** – moves **more slowly than low orbit**
  – greater distance to travel
  – time for orbit longer

When the Moon passes between Sun and Earth a **solar** eclipse occurs

Examiner's tip

There may well be a question on uses of satellites

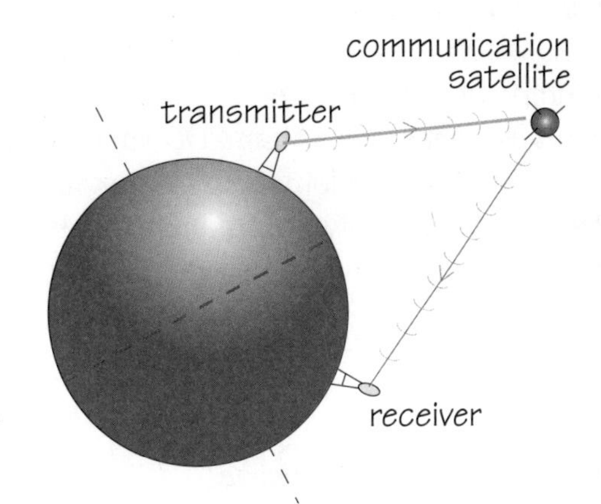

- **Uses** – **beam information** e.g. TV to places on Earth a long way apart
  – **monitor conditions** e.g. weather on Earth
  – **act as observatory** since no disturbance from atmosphere
- **Orbits** – **communication** satellite uses **high equatorial** orbit; scans same point continuously. Orbit is said to be 'geostationary' since time of rotation is same as that of Earth. Early communication satellites passive reflectors; modern satellites use solar power to amplify signals
  – **monitoring** satellite uses **low polar** orbit; scans whole N or S hemisphere each day to monitor movements of clouds and weather patterns.
  Low orbit time of 96 minutes means Earth spins through 24° in this time; satellite sees changing view of Earth's surface in successive orbits

Orbital motion

- **Planetary orbits** – **elliptical** not circular
- **Comets** – balls of ice and dust
  – diameter a few kilometres
  – orbit **very** eccentric (Sun not at centre)
  – much closer to Sun at times → visible
- **Orbit larger** – **further** from Sun e.g. Pluto
  – **longer time** for orbit

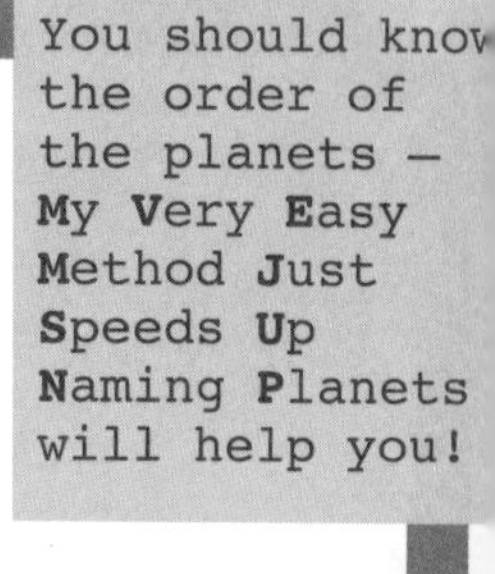

- **Small bodies** e.g. satellites – **need certain speed** to stay in orbit

Note that the orbit of Pluto is at an angle to those of the other planets

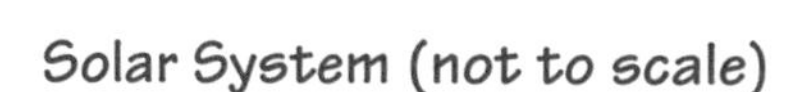

Solar System (not to scale)

- **Solar System** – Sun and planets
  – also other bodies such as asteroids
- **Asteroids** – lumps of rock and ice
  – largest ones more than 200 km in diameter
  – smallest a few kilometres in diameter
- **Inner planets** – first four; only Earth and Mars have moons
- **Outer planets** – last five; all have moons (Jupiter has at least sixteen)

Gravity

- **Attractive force**
- **Acts between** – **all bodies** in universe
  – **Sun and planets**, where gravity provides the centripetal force needed to keep planets in orbit
  – **planets** where gravity causes changes in orbits when planets get near each other (also used to give space rockets extra velocity)
  – **Stars and galaxies**
- **Gravitational force (g) greater if**
  – **mass** of bodies **greater**
  – **distance** apart **less**; 2 x distance means a quarter of the force
- **Earth** – **g = 10 N/kg**
- **Larger planets** e.g. Jupiter – **g greater**
- **Smaller planets** e.g. Mercury – **g smaller**
- **Weight** – **force caused by gravity** acting on a mass
  – weight is the pull of the planet on a body
  – weight on larger planets greater
  – weight on smaller planets (and our Moon) smaller
  (g on Moon = $^1/_6$ x g on earth)
- **Weightlessness** – **no weight**
  – no force exerted on surface – pulling body down
  – orbiting satellite – astronauts exert no force because they and spacecraft accelerate towards Earth's centre; acceleration caused by gravitational force so both fall freely at same rate (same as people in lift where cable snapped and lift falls down shaft!)
  – far out in space where gravity (practically) zero

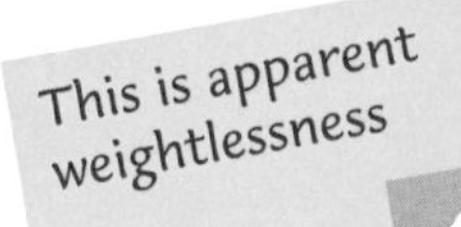

This is true weightlessness

The Universe

Stars

Our galaxy (Milky Way) would look like this from space

- **Sun** – one of millions of stars
- **Galaxy** – group of stars
  – stars millions of times further apart than planets from Sun
- **Cluster** – group of galaxies
  – Milky Way in cluster with about twenty other galaxies
  – some contain thousands of galaxies
- **Universe** – at least one thousand million (billion) galaxies
  – galaxies millions of times further apart than stars
- **Gravitational force** – acts between stars and between galaxies
  – distances between stars very large but they are massive bodies so forces quite strong
  – all stars orbit centre of galaxy at about same speed unlike planets in solar system where inner planets orbit faster than outer planets (suggests mass of galaxy not concentrated near middle but is spread out evenly)

Life of a star

- **Birth:** – dust + gas —immense gravity→ star
- **Mass** – very large compared to planets; planets may form at same time from smaller masses
- **Volume** – Sun (small star) million times larger volume than Earth
- **Density** – star matter **millions of times denser than Earth** matter
- **Heat** – stars are balls of **very hot gases**
  – creates forces tending to **expansion** of Star
  – forces balance → **stability** (e.g. our Sun)
- **Size change** – **stable** for millions of years
  – **expansion** → **red giant** → **rapid contraction** → **supernova explosion**

red giant ↓ **contraction** ↓ **white dwarf** (very small, cold)

rapid contraction (if red giant is massive enough) → supernova explosion ↓ **neutron star** (very dense) ↓ **black hole** (no light escapes)

Examiner's tip

Make sure your answers only contain the important key points

Energy production in a star

- **Light nuclei** – fuse → heavier nuclei
  – vast energy release

Nuclear fusion is not the same process as nuclear fission (which occurs in nuclear power stations)

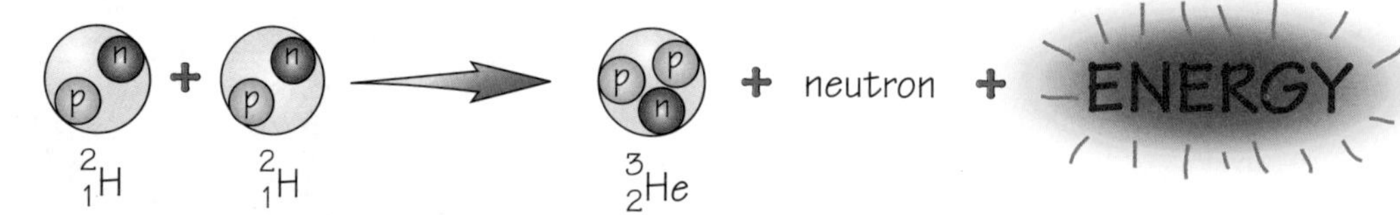

Origin of the universe

- **Red shift** – light from other galaxies shifted to red end of visible spectrum
- **More red shift** – galaxies further away → galaxies receding fast → universe expanding
  – gravitational forces tend to try to pull them together so expansion being slowed down
- **Big Bang** – theory on possible start of universe
  – uses red shift observations; amount of red shift used to work out speed of recession of galaxies (Edwin Hubble)
  – universe began from explosion of matter
- **Age** – at least 15 billion years old – calculated from the rate of expansion
- **Other evidence for Big Bang** – microwave background radiation detected – it fills space and is believed to be energy left over from explosion
- **Future of universe** – depends on amount of mass in universe and speed of recession of galaxies

Some scientists believe that the universe has always existed — this is called the Steady State theory

Questions

1 One use of artificial satellites is to carry information around the world.

(a) What is the name we give to this type of satellite? ______________________

(b) Name and describe the use of one other type of satellite.

____

____

2 Astronauts in an orbiting spacecraft feel weightless.

(a) What does this mean?

____

(b) The spacecraft is still within the gravitational field of the Earth. Explain why the astronauts are apparently weightless.

____

____

3 Halley's comet is seen in the sky every 75 years.

(a) With the aid of a diagram explain why it is seen only periodically and not all the time.

(b) On your diagram draw the path of a second comet that would only ever be seen once from the Earth.

4 Describe the stages in the evolution of a star resulting in the formation of a neutron star.

____

____

____

____

____

____

Energy resources and energy transfer

Kinetic theory

- All substances made of particles in motion

Brownian motion

- **Robert Brown** – **studied pollen** grains in water
  – pollen grains in constant, random motion
  – movement caused by water molecules therefore water molecules in constant random motion

Solids

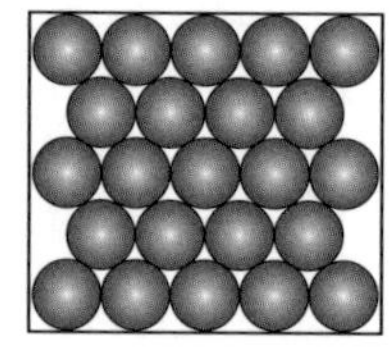

- **Fixed arrangements** of particles
- Particles vibrate about fixed positions
- Strong forces hold particles together
- Difficult to compress

Liquids

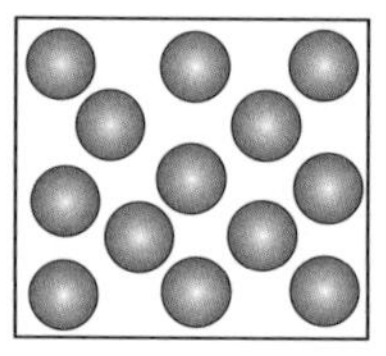

- **Particles not in fixed positions**
- Particles jostle, change position
- Difficult to compress

Gases

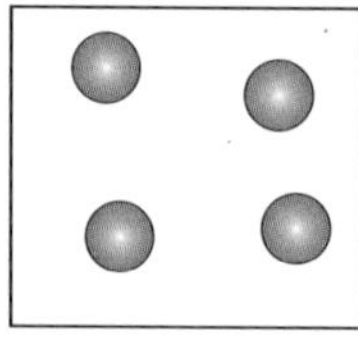

- **Particles normally widely spaced**
- Forces between particles negligible
- No fixed shape
- Easily compressed

Change of state

- **Temperature increase** – **energy** of particles **increases**
  – amplitude of vibration of solid particles increases
  – particles interchange positions → melting to liquid state
  – liquid particles move faster → gas state

Thermal energy

- **Thermal energy** – transferred from **hot to** *cold body*
- **Temperature differences** – may be caused by energy transfer
- 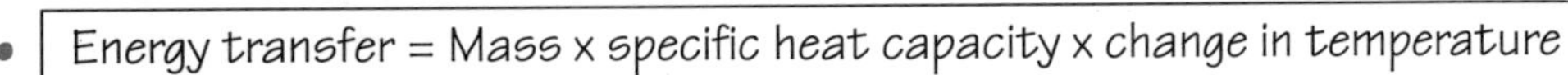
  Energy transfer = Mass x specific heat capacity x change in temperature

Units are J/kg/°C. Different materials have different values water = 4200 J/kg/°C

Conduction

- **Transfer of energy** by substance where substance itself does not move
- ***Occurs in all materials***
- **Metal** – ***good conductor***
  - **hotter** → **more kinetic energy (KE)** for free electrons → ***diffusion***
  - ***also energy transfer by collision of adjacent electrons***
  - different metals conduct at different rates – copper and aluminum used to make saucepans/frying pans as they are very good conductors

Note that even metallic liquids such as mercury are good conductors

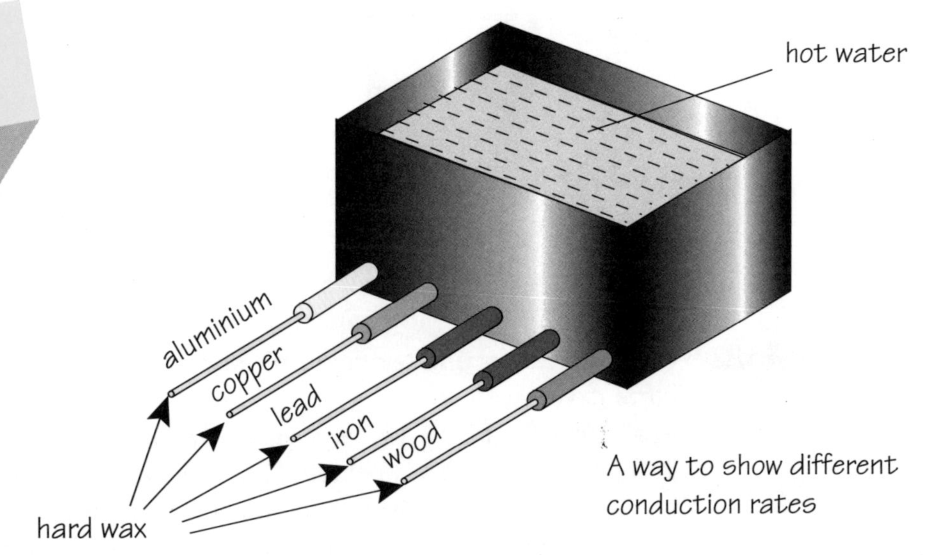

A way to show different conduction rates

- **Non-metal solid** – atoms rigidly held together
  - vibrating atoms pass on vibrations to adjacent atoms
  - no free electrons so process slower than in metals
  - ***poor conductor***
- **Non-metal liquid** – particles further apart than in solid
  - ***poor conductor***
- ***Gas*** – particles very far apart
  - ***very poor conductor***
- **Insulator** – any substance that is a ***poor conductor*** e.g. wood, cork, plastic
  - some substances trap tiny pockets of air between fibres (air is a gas so is very poor conductor) e.g. wool, glass fibre – they are good insulators
  - US Space Shuttle becomes very hot on entering Earth's atmosphere – special tiles stop overheating (you could heat tile with a blowlamp and pick it up without burning yourself!)

- **Some materials** are **neither** good conductors nor good insulators – their conductivity lies in between
- **Choice** – which conductor to use depends on factors other than conductivity – manufacturers must consider cost and durability for example: copper is best conductor but expensive, central heating radiators are made from steel as it is cheap, easily shaped and stands up to knocks

Convection

- **Gas/liquid** – **can flow**
  - **carry energy** from hot areas to cold areas
  - **particles gain KE** → **expansion**
  - **hotter parts** less dense → **rise up** through colder parts
  - **colder parts** more dense → **replace hotter parts**
- **Water heated** – dye rises as water expands
  - dye falls as water cools down
- **Ice cube melted** – coloured ice melts: cold water falls as it is more dense
  - coloured water rises as water warms up

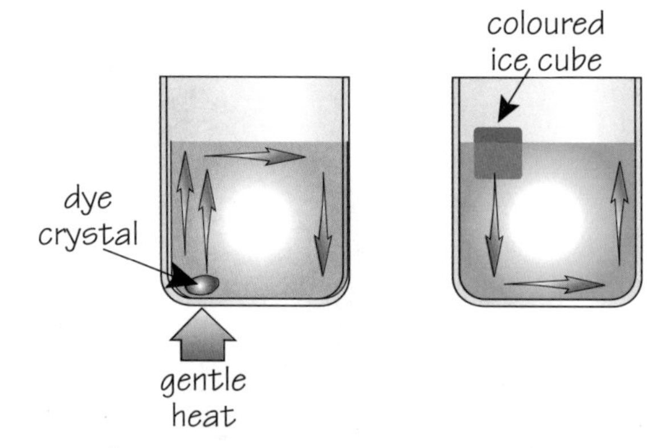

- **Examples** – central heating radiator heats air which circulates by convection currents
  - sea breezes – during day land warms up more than sea (takes a lot of heat to raise temperature of sea) causing the air over land to rise up – cold air over sea moves in to replace it – therefore breezes during day tend to blow from sea to land (opposite at night)

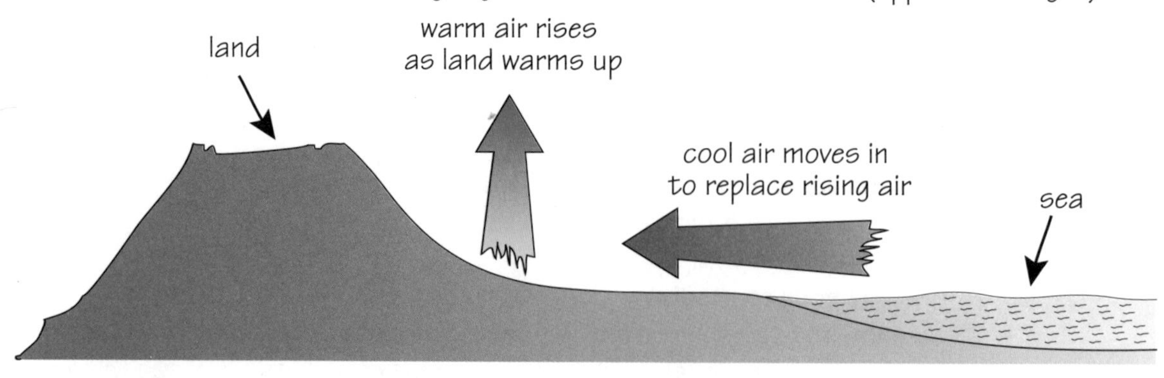

Applying your knowledge of thermal transfer is important in exam questions

  - hot air balloon – air inside heated by burner becomes less dense and rises, taking balloon with it

Radiation

- **Energy transfer by waves**
- **Part of electromagnetic spectrum** (infra-red, IR)
  - detected by skin as IR invisible
  - travels in straight lines (at speed of light) – so no good for heating a whole room since only heats those parts it can get to in a straight line – convection better method
  - can travel through empty space – energy from Sun is radiated to us
- **Dark matt surfaces** – **good radiators**
  – **good absorbers**
  (poor reflectors)
- **Light, shiny surfaces** – **poor radiators**
  – **good reflectors**
  (poor absorbers)
- **Applications** – car radiators painted black to radiate heat away quickly
  - kettles shiny (if metal) to avoid too much heat loss
  - solar panels painted black to absorb maximum amount of Sun's radiated energy
  - thermograms are photographs taken by emitted radiation from object – used in medicine and meteorology

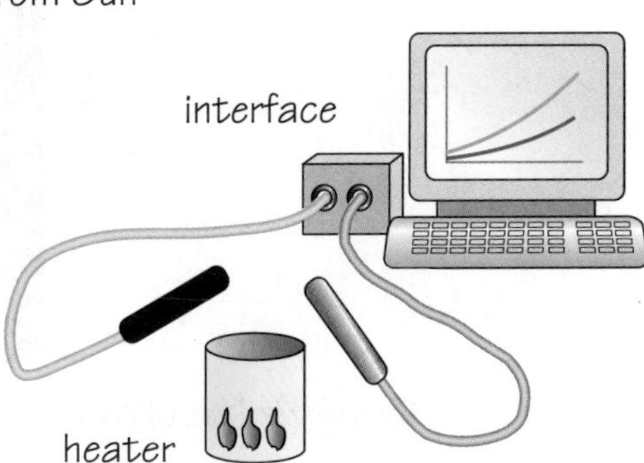

Black temperature probe absorbs more heat energy than shiny probe

House insulation

- **Radiation** – losses small so can be neglected
- **Conduction/convection** – need to be reduced
- **Energy flow**
  - at steady temperature, rate of flow out = rate of flow in
  - insulation means less energy flow out so less energy needed to heat i.e. reduced fuel bills
- **Loft insulation**
  - most cost-effective way; if no insulation, energy conducted through ceiling and transferred to roof by convection
  - use fibre glass; trapped air cannot form convection currents so only conduction (air is poor conductor)

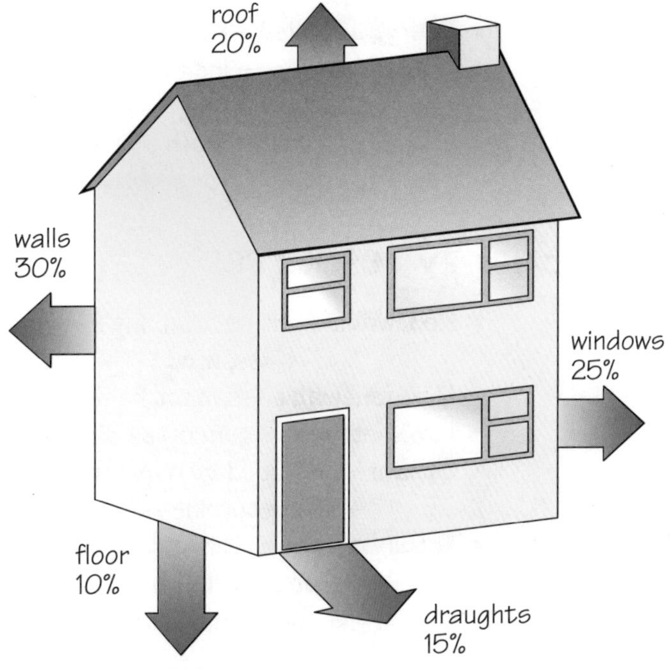

Examiner's tip

Exam questions are often set on methods of insulating buildings

- **Double glazing** – may cost several thousand pounds for average house, so not cost-effective
  – double pane traps air – air gap thin to reduce convection
- **Other methods** – draught proofing around doors/windows
  – carpets/curtains
  – porch

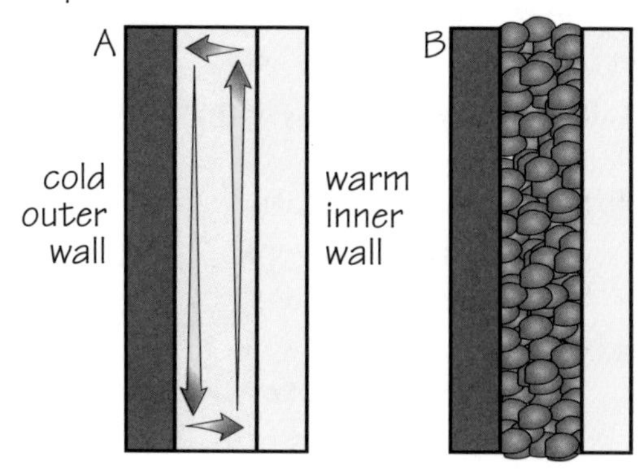

- **Cavity wall insulation** – houses are double-walled
  – gap called cavity
  – if air in gap convection currents transfer energy from inside (diagram A)
  – fill gap with mineral wool/foam to stop convection (diagram B)

Energy efficiency

$$\text{Efficiency} = \frac{\text{useful energy transferred} \times 100\%}{\text{total energy supplied}}$$

- **Unuseful energy** – wasted
  – reduces efficiency
- **Energy supplied** – heats surroundings
  – increasingly spread out
  – more difficult to use for energy transfer

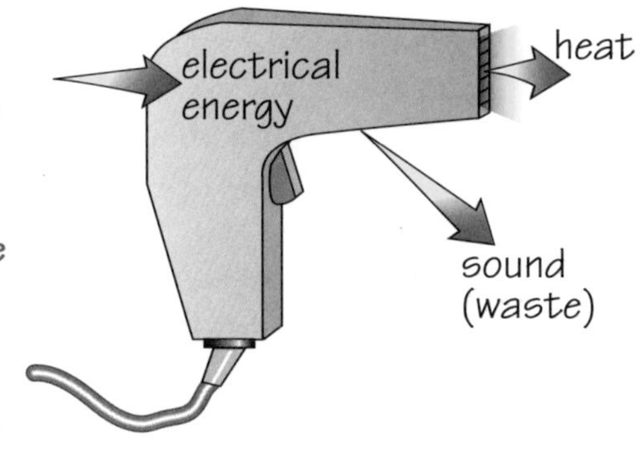

Energy resources

- **Renewable** – will not run out e.g. wood, tides, wind
- **Non-renewable** – cannot be replaced e.g. fossil fuels, nuclear
- **Power station** – generates electricity from both types
- **Steam** – produced by non-renewable resources + wood/geothermal
  – drives turbines
- **Turbines** – driven directly by renewable resources
  – solar cells produce electricity directly
  – turn generators → electricity

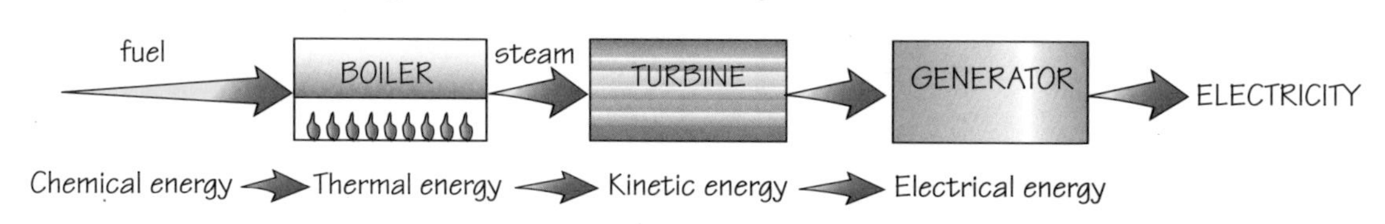

Non-renewable versus **Renewable**

Non-renewable:
- Will run out
- Waste
- Fuel costs
- Transportation
- Building costs high

Renewable:
- Will not run out
- No waste
- No fuel costs
- No transportation
- Generating equipment costs high

(note: above excludes wood)

- Nuclear power – fuel costs low
  – cost of initial building high
  – cost of decommissioning station at end of useful life high
  – environmental costs
- Solar cells – expensive
  – often good way to generate electricity
- Tidal barrage – water flows from high to low level
- Geothermal – hot rocks below surface of Earth
  – energy released by decay of radioactive elements
  – slower process than in nuclear reactor
  – water pumped through hot rocks
  – steam produced drives turbines

Examiner's tip

You should be able to identify and evaluate costs of different energy resources

Work

Work done = force x distance
= energy transferred

- Units – joules (J)
- 1 J = 1 Nm

Power = work done/time taken
= rate of energy transfer

- Units – watts (W)
- 1 W = 1 J/s

A ramp is a machine. Machines make work easier. Other examples include: spanner, pulley, lever

Kinetic energy (KE)

- Moving object has KE
- KE depends on mass and speed

$KE = \frac{1}{2} \times mass \times (speed)^2$

- Units – J
- Example – moving car

Examiner's tip

Students often forget that speed must be squared

Potential energy (PE)

- **Gravitational PE** – energy stored
  – depends on weight + height
  – example: walking upstairs

Gravitational PE = weight x change in vertical height

- **Units** – J

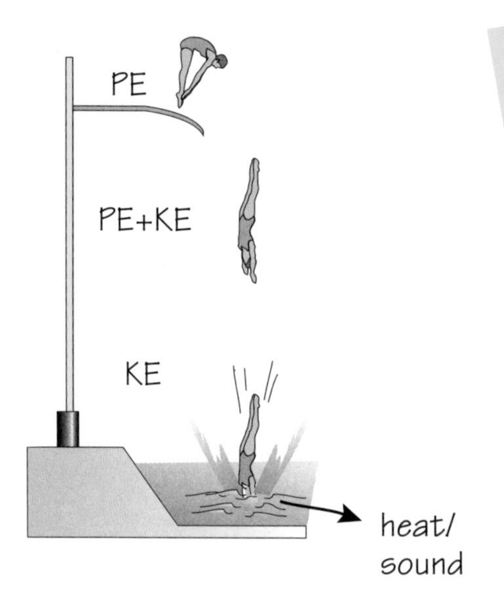

A high diver exchanges her PE for KE on the way down

- **Weight depends on** – mass
  – gravitational field strength, *g*

Weight = mass x *g*

- **Gravitational field strength** – on Earth about 10 N/kg
  – on Moon about 1.7 N/kg
- **Elastic PE** – energy stored
  – depends on change in shape of body
  – examples: stretched spring, catapult

Questions

1 A 'radiator' used in home central heating should really be called a 'convector'. Do you agree? Explain your answer.

____

____

2 An electric kettle is rated at 1 kW.
It takes 30 s to heat up a certain mass of water.

(a) If 1 W = 1 J/s, how much energy is supplied to the kettle?

____

(b) 10 kJ of energy is wasted. Calculate the efficiency of the kettle.

____

(c) i) How is this energy wasted? ______________________________

ii) How could this waste be reduced? ______________________________

3 (a) Name a renewable energy resource. ______________________________

(b) Describe three main advantages that renewable energy resources have over non-renewable resources for the generation of electricity.

i) ______________________________

ii) ______________________________

iii) ______________________________

4 Julie runs up a staircase. Each step is 20 cm high. There are 10 steps to the top. If her mass is 45 kg,

(a) what is her weight (g = 10 N/kg)?

____

(b) how much work must she do to reach the top?

____

____

____

20 cm

(c) what power does she develop if it takes her 3 s?

____

____

____

(d) at what average speed is she moving vertically upwards?

____

____

(e) what kinetic energy does she have?

____

____

Radioactivity

Atomic structure

- **Atoms** – tiny central **nucleus** with electrons outside
- **Radioactivity** – emitted when **nucleus changes**
  – some substances emit radiation, these are said to be radioactive
- **Nucleus** – **protons** (p) + **neutrons** (n)
- **Electrons** (e) – **orbit around nucleus**
- **Plum pudding model** – plums (**electrons**) **embedded** in atom
- **Alpha scattering** – alpha particles (see below) fired at thin gold foil
  – small fraction scattered through very large angles

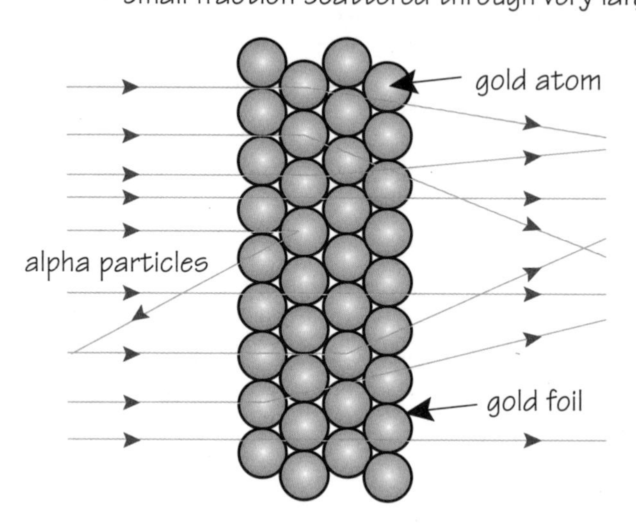

– Rutherford suggested scattering due to repulsion from high concentration of positive charge – implies electrons at very large distance from nucleus

	Mass	Charge
p	1	+1
n	1	0
e	negligible	–1

Number of p = number of e; overall charge on atom is zero

Elements

- **Proton number** – **same** for atoms of **same element**
- **Nucleon (mass) number** – total **number of p + n**
- **Isotope** – atoms of **same element** with **different** number of **n**
- **Radioactive isotope** – isotopes with **unstable nuclei**
  – also known as **radioisotope** or **radionuclide**
- **Disintegration** – **nuclei break up** → number of **n and p may change** → **different element** if p changes
- **Radiation emission** – **continually**
  – **random**
  – radioactive substance emits radiation whatever is done to it

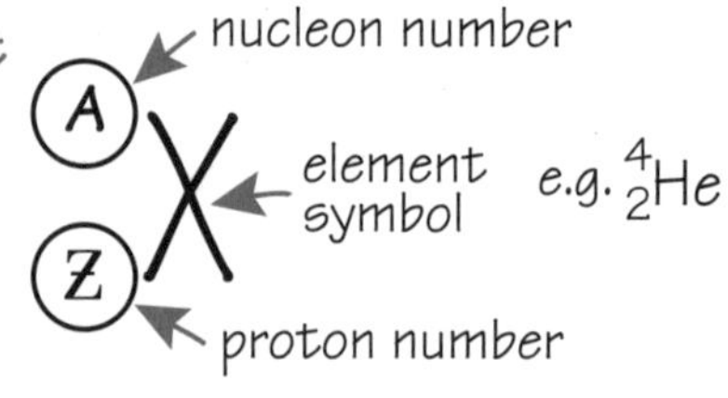

Types of radiation

Note that γ decay has no affect on nucleon or proton number

Type	Symbol	Stopped by	Composition	Charge	Mass
alpha	α	thin sheet of paper	2p + 2n (He nucleus)	+	large
beta	ß	2 mm metal	electrons; n → p + e	–	tiny
gamma	γ	reduced by thick concrete/lead	Em radiation	0	0

Look at composition to predict new proton and nucleon numbers as a result of decay

Sources of radiation

- **All living things** are radioactive
- **Radioactive substances are all around us**
- **Space** – cosmic rays
  – constant stream
  – some difficult to detect
- **Ground/building materials** – many rocks in Earth's crust are radioactive
  – high levels of radioactivity in areas built on granite
- **Food**
- **Medical** – radiography e.g. chest X-ray
  – treatment e.g. cancer
- **Nuclear power station**

Radiation is a natural part of our environment; it is called 'background radiation'

Radiation hazard warning sign

Warning notices must be displayed when radioactive sources are used

Dangers of radiation

- **Absorption** by material – collision with neutral atoms/molecules
  – atoms/molecules may become charged (ionised)
  – if living material, cell damage may result
- **Cell damage** – may kill/cause cancer
  – alpha source most dangerous in body; although not very penetrating, it is strongly ionising and is particularly dangerous if inhaled but is generally least dangerous outside the body
  – beta, gamma sources most dangerous outside body because they can reach the cells of organs in the body and be absorbed by them; if inside body, they are less dangerous because cells likely to absorb radiation

Half-life

- **Activity measured with Geiger-Müller (GM) tube** and counter as shown

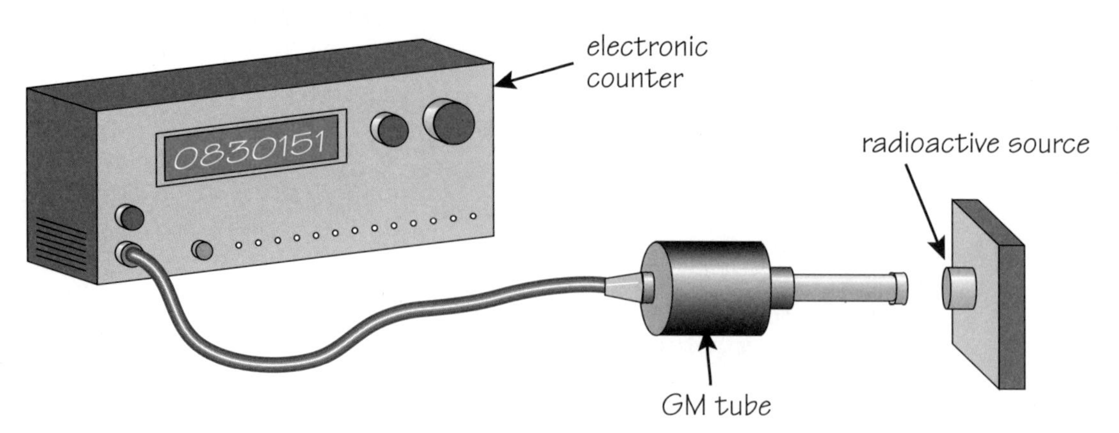

- **Radioactive atoms** → **radiation** → **stable** (non-radioactive atoms)
- **Activity decreases with time**
- **Half-life** – **time** for activity/count rate **to halve**
  - different for different radioisotopes e.g. Na-24 is 15 hours, Pt-239 is 24000 years
- **Carbon dating** – half-life 5730 years
  - used to find **age of once living radioactive materials**

In practice, background count should be subtracted

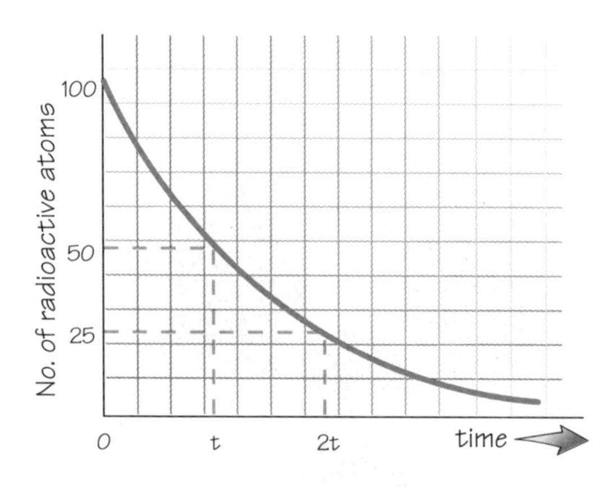

The graph shows the decay of a radionuclide. Half-life = t

Uses of radiation

- **Monitor/control thickness** – greater absorption by thicker material
  - alpha and beta
- **Medical treatment** – kill cancer cells
  - gamma e.g. cobalt 60, also used to sterilise medical equipment such as surgeon's instruments (packed into plastic bags and irradiated to kill bacteria)
- **Tracers** – trace path of fluids
  - medicine, e.g. iodine 131 used to see if thyroid gland working satisfactorily (has short half-life)
  - industry to detect leaks in pipes
  - agriculture e.g radioactive phosphorus used to show how well plants absorb phosphorus

Examiner's tip

You should be able to evaluate appropriateness of sources for different uses

Nuclear fission

- Neutrons – fired at large nucleus
- Nucleus splits → neutrons released
  → chain reaction
- New atoms also radioactive
- Energy released – much larger than associated with a chemical bond
- Nuclear power stations release energy by nuclear fission
- Sun releases energy by nuclear fusion

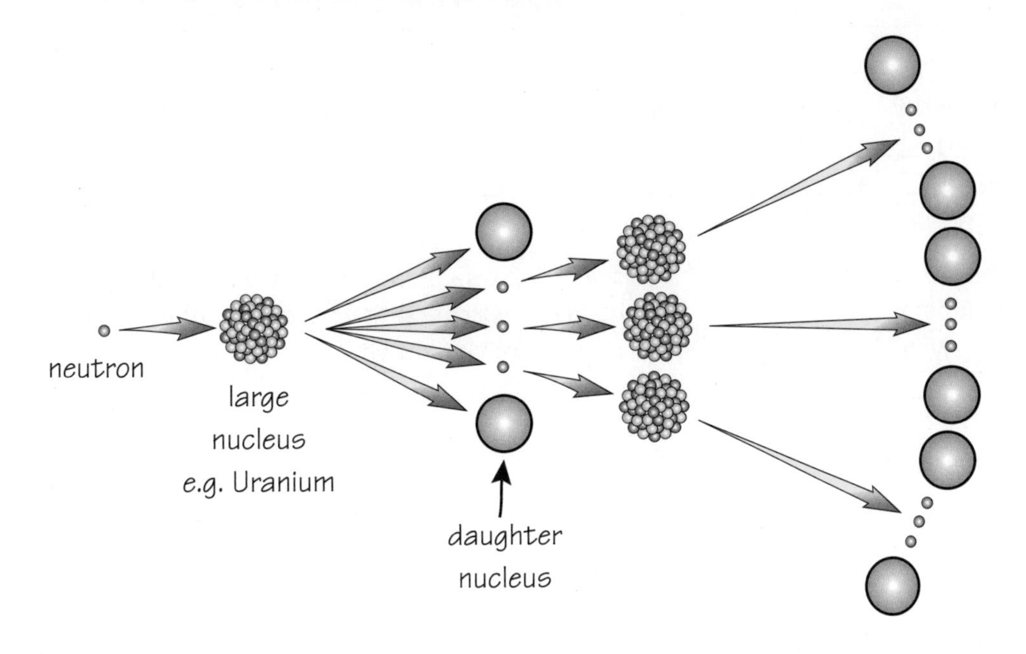

In a nuclear power station, the chain reaction is slowed/stopped by control rods; they absorb the neutrons

Questions

1 (a) Describe the 'plum pudding' model of the atom.

(b) How was this model modified by the alpha scattering experiments?

2 Name two ways in which gamma radiation differs from either alpha or beta radiation.

i)

ii)

3 The activity of a sample of a radionuclide was measured. It was found to be 3000 counts/min at 9 am. By 11 am this had decreased to 750 counts/min.

(a) What instrument is used to measure the activity?

(b) Calculate the half-life of the sample.

(c) When the detector was moved away, the experimenter noticed that it still recorded a low count rate. Why?

4 Steel sheets are produced in a steel mill. The sheets are rolled out to a certain thickness as they pass along a conveyor belt. By drawing a diagram, explain how a radioactive source can be used to monitor and control the thickness.

Answers

Electricity and magnetism

1 Negative charges on rod transfer to cloth – makes cloth –ve and rod +ve

2 (a) 6 V
(b) Current through each lamp = 1.5 A
$R = V/I$
$= 6/1.5$
$= 4\ \Omega$

3 (a) $I = P/V$
$= 1500/250$
$= 6$ A
Use 10 A fuse
(b) 7 days @ ⅓ hour per day = 7/3 hours
Cost = 1.52 x 7/3 x 6p
= 21 p

4 (a) Output voltage bigger than input voltage
(b) Number of turns needed =
$\frac{7.0}{2.0} \times 100 = 350$

5 (a) Divides up the battery voltage; pd shared between components
(b) jThermistor heated
→ resistance decreases
→ pd across thermistor decreases ($V \alpha R$)
→ pd across transistor decreases
→ transistor switches off
→ LED goes out
(c) NOT gate

Forces and motion

1 (a) Constant acceleration
(b) i) Acceleration = 6/30
= 0.2 m/s^2
ii) Distance = area under graph
= area of triangle
= ½ x 30 x 6
= 90 m

2 (a) Resultant force = 6500 – 850
= 5650 N
Acceleration = F/m
= 5650/1200
= 4.71 m/s^2
(b) Reaction time, weather, condition of tyres/brakes/road

3 ↻ moment = 120 x 0.5
= 60 Nm
↺ moment = W x 1.25
= 1.25W Nm
To balance, 1.25W = 60
W = 48 N

4 Momentum before collision
= 5000 x 10 + 3000 x 5
= 50 000 + 15 000
= 65 000 kgm/s
Momentum after collision
= 8000 x v kgm/s
Conservation of momentum →
8000 v = 65 000
v = 8.13 m/s

5 Force = $\frac{0.4}{0.1} \times 150$
= 4 x 150
= 600 N

Waves

1 **(a)** i) Wavelength = 2.7 cm
ii) Amplitude = 0.75 cm
(b) i) $1\frac{1}{2}$ wavelengths fit on screen in 0.01 s
so, 1 wavelength takes $\frac{2}{3} \times 0.01$ s

$$\text{frequency} = \frac{1}{\frac{2}{3} \times 0.01} = \frac{3}{0.02} = 150 \text{ Hz}$$

ii) Speed = 150 x 2.7
= 405 m/s

2 **(a)**

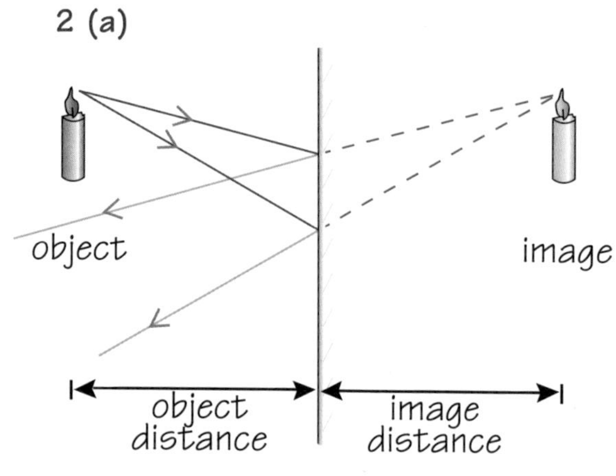

(b) Virtual. Not really there/cannot be projected on a screen.

3 **(a)** (Ultrasonic) pulse sent into water
Time to return to receiver measured
Depth of shoal = speed x time
(b) 0.3 s for signal to travel there and back
Use time = 0.15 s
Depth = 1550 x 0.15
= 232.5 m

4 P – longitudinal
– fast
– travel through solids + liquids

S – transverse
– slow
– travel only through solids

The Earth and beyond

1 **(a)** Communications satellite
(b) Monitoring – gather Earth data on e.g. weather
Observatory – gather space data on e.g. planets

2 **(a)** No weight
(b) Spacecraft pulled towards Earth by gravitational force
Astronauts pulled towards spacecraft
Floor falls away as fast as astronauts fall towards floor
No contact with floor
Therefore zero weight

3 **(a)** Long elliptical orbit
only visible when near Earth

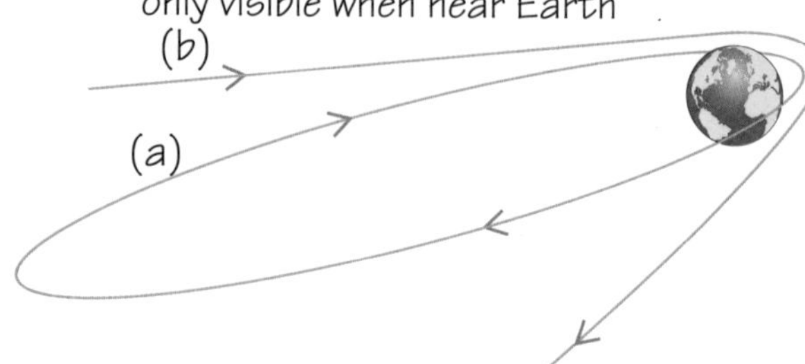

(b) Parabolic path – never returns.

4 Dust + gas → star born
↓
expansion ← stability
↓
red giant → rapid contraction
→ supernova

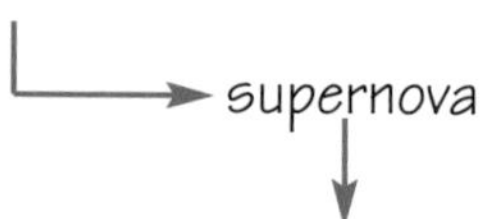

Energy resources and energy transfer

1 Yes – little radiated heat – room mainly heated by creation of convection current

2 (a) 1 kW = 1000 W
Energy supplied = 1000 x 30 s
= 30000 J
= 30 kJ

(b) Efficiency $= \frac{10 \text{ kJ}}{30 \text{ kJ}} \times 100$
= 33 %

(c) i) Heats up kettle body/surroundings
sound energy produced
ii) Insulate kettle e.g. wrap insulation around

3 (a) Any of wind, wave, tidal, geothermal, solar, wood
(b) Will not run out, no waste, no fuel cost, no transportation cost

4 (a) Weight = 45 x 10 = 450 N

(b) Work = force x distance
= 450 x 10 x 0.2
= 900 J

(c) Power $= \frac{\text{work done}}{\text{time taken}}$
= 900/3
= 300 W

(d) Average speed $= \frac{2\text{m}}{3\text{s}}$
= 0.67m/s

(e) Kinetic energy $= \frac{1}{2} \times 45 \times (\frac{2}{3})^2$
= 10J

Radioactivity

1 (a) Plums = electrons
electrons embedded in atom
(b) Atom has central nucleus
nucleus tiny
nucleus +ve
electrons orbit nucleus
most of atom empty space

2 Gamma – wave not particle
– no mass/charge
– travels at speed of light/ 3×10^8 m/s

3 (a) GM tube/counter
(b) 9am – 3000 counts/min
11am – 750 counts/min
Therefore 2 hours → drops to ¼
1 hour → drops to ½
half-life = 1 hour
(c) Recording background radiation

4 radioactive source

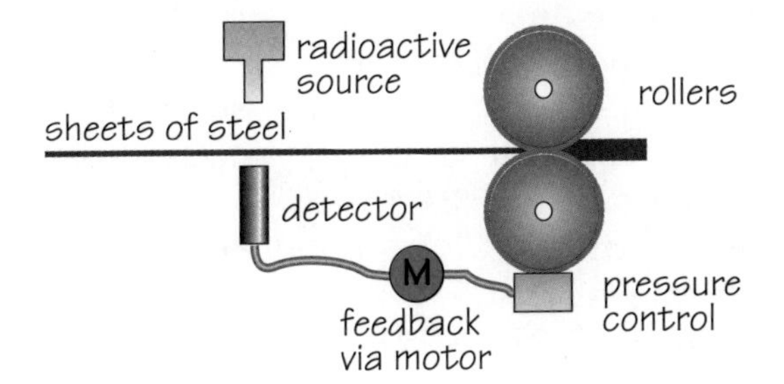

source above/below sheets
detector below/above sheets
correct thickness → p counts/min recorded
thickness too big → fewer than p recorded
thickness too small → more than p recorded
link detector via feedback to motor
motor controls roller pressure

Index

These pages can be used for your own notes.

NOTES

Success or your money back

Letts' market leading series GCSE Revision Notes gives you everything you need for exam success. We're so confident that they're the best revision books you can buy that if you don't make the grade we will give you your money back!

HERE'S HOW IT WORKS

Register the Letts GCSE Revision Notes you buy by writing to us within 28 days of purchase with the following information:

- Name
- Address
- Postcode
- Subject of GCSE Revision Notes book bought – please include your till receipt or school name and address and subject teacher
- Probable tier you will enter

To make a **claim**, compare your results to the grades below. If any of your grades qualify for a refund, make a claim by writing to us within 28 days of getting your results, enclosing a copy of your original exam slip. If you do not register, you won't be able to make a claim after you receive your results.

CLAIM IF…

You're a Higher Tier student and get a grade D or below
You're an Intermediate Tier student and get a grade E or below
You're a Foundation Tier student and get a grade F or below
You're a Scottish Standard Grade Student taking Credit and General Level exams and get a grade 4 or below
This offer is not open to Scottish Standard Grade students sitting Foundation Level exams.

Registration and claim address:
Letts Success or Your Money Back Offer, Letts Educational, Aldine Place, London W12 8AW

TERMS AND CONDITIONS

1 Applies to the Letts GCSE Revision Notes series only
2 Registration of purchases must be received by Letts Educational within 28 days of the purchase date
3 Registration must be accompanied by a valid till receipt
4 All money back claims must be received by Letts Educational within 28 days of receiving exam results
5 All claims must be accompanied by a letter stating the claim and a copy of the relevant exam results slip
6 Claims will be invalid if they do not match with the original registered subjects
7 Letts Educational reserves the right to seek confirmation of the level of entry of the claimant
8 Responsibility cannot be accepted for lost, delayed or damaged applications, or applications received outside of the stated registration / claim timescales
9 Proof of posting will not be accepted as proof of delivery
10 Offer only available to GCSE students studying within the UK
11 SUCCESS OR YOUR MONEY BACK is promoted by Letts Educational, Aldine Place, London W12 8AW
12 Registration indicates a complete acceptance of these rules
13 Illegible entries will be disqualified
14 In all matters, the decision of Letts Educational will be final and no correspondence will be entered into

Letts Educational
Aldine Place
London W12 8AW
Tel: 020 8740 2266
Fax: 020 8743 8451
email: mail@lettsed.co.uk
website: www.letts-education.com

First published 1998
Reprinted 1998, 1999
New edition 1999
This edition 2000

Editorial and design by Hart McLeod, Cambridge

British Library Cataloguing in Publication Data
A CIP record for this book is available from the British Library.

ISBN 1 84085 475 8

Printed in Italy

Letts Educational Limited is a division of Granada Learning Limited, part of the Granada Media Group.